Modern Cabinetmaking

Frameless and Traditional Construction

KEN CALHOUN

Professor of Industrial
and Engineering Technology
Central Washington University

PTR Prentice Hall, Englewood Cliffs, New Jersey 07632

Library of Congress Cataloging-in-Publication Data

CALHOUN, KEN.
   Modern cabinetmaking : frameless and traditional construction /
Ken Calhoun
     p.   cm.
   Includes index.
   ISBN 0-13-292749-7
   1. Cabinetwork. I. Title.
TT197.C244 1993   92-27702
   684.1′6—dc20   CIP

Editorial/production supervision
  and interior design: *Barbara Marttine*
Cover design: *Ben Santora*
Acquisitions editor: *Bernard Goodwin*
Manufacturing buyer: *Mary McCartney*

©1993 by PTR Prentice-Hall, Inc.
A Simon & Schuster Company
Englewood Cliffs, New Jersey 07632

The publisher offers discounts on this book when ordered
in bulk quantities. For more information, contact:

Corporate Sales Department
PTR Prentice Hall
113 Sylvan Avenue
Englewood Cliffs, NJ 07632

Phone: 201-592-2863
Fax: 201-592-2249

Printed in the United States of America

10 9 8 7 6 5 4 3 2 1

ISBN   0-13-292749-7

Prentice-Hall International (UK) Limited, *London*
Prentice-Hall of Australia Pty. Limited, *Sydney*
Prentice-Hall Canada Inc., *Toronto*
Prentice-Hall Hispanoamericana, S.A., *Mexico*
Prentice-Hall of India Private Limited, *New Delhi*
Prentice-Hall of Japan, Inc., *Tokyo*
Simon & Schuster Asia Pte. Ltd., *Singapore*
Editora Prentice-Hall do Brasil, Ltda., *Rio de Janeiro*

Contents

SECTION TWO
Construction of Frameless Cabinets

═══════════════════════════════

SECTION THREE
Construction of Face-Frame Cabinets

SECTION FOUR
Computers

Preface

The new frameless cabinetmaking system is proving to be quite a radical departure from the traditional face-frame system. One of the major benefits of the frameless system is the potential for some very significant cost savings. Some experts estimate a 50% savings in labor for frameless cabinets. This is brought about by the fact that it takes a great deal less labor time to make frameless cabinets and the skill-level requirement of much of the labor is lower.

Additionally, the materials used are often less expensive, and there is less use of expensive hardwood lumber. Since most of the material used requires no additional finishing, another expensive step is eliminated.

Finally, the frameless system lends itself well to making knocked-down (KD) or ready-to-assemble (RTA) cabinets that can be shipped in knocked-down form and easily assembled on the job site. This can result in a considerable savings in shipping costs.

Many shops have switched exclusively to the frameless system; others are building framelesss cabinets but also continue to build face-frame cabinets for customers who prefer the traditional appearance of face-frame cabinets. Still other shops are faced with the decision of whether or not to switch to building frameless cabinets.

This book compares the two systems and presents proven, successful techniques for using either system.

The book is divided into four sections. The first section compares the two systems and presents a comprehensive description of the materials and hardware used in both systems.

The second section presents a detailed description of the construction of frameless cabinets. Since some of the equipment used is quite different from that used in building face-frame cabinets, options for small, medium, and large shops are presented in this section.

The third section presents the construction of traditional face-frame cabinets.

The fourth section shows how computers can be used as a sales tool, for preparing estimates, for preparing shop drawings and cutting lists, and even for operating cutting equipment.

The photography, unless credited otherwise, was done by Debbie Storlie.

Ken Calhoun

SECTION ONE

A Comparison of the Frameless and the Face-Frame Cabinetmaking Systems

The new frameless cabinetmaking system represents the most significant change in the cabinetmaking industry in many years. Users of the frameless system are required to become familiar with new construction techniques, the use of different machinery, the use of different materials and hardware and, in some cases, they must learn a new measuring system.

The new frameless system offers the potential for great savings in labor costs and for some savings in material costs.

However, some customers prefer the appearance of traditional face-frame cabinets, so some shops have elected to continue building conventional face-frame cabinets. Yet other shops offer both types.

Section one includes Chapters 1 to 4 and presents a comparison of the two systems. Chapter 1 introduces the frameless system, and Chapter 2 describes the system in much more detail. Chapter 3 presents a detailed description of the face-frame system. Chapter 4 presents information on the materials used in both systems.

CHAPTER 1

Introduction
to the Frameless System

BACKGROUND OF THE FRAMELESS SYSTEM

The invention of the modern frameless cabinetmaking system is generally attributed to Paul Hettich of West Germany. This system, also known as System 32 or the 32-mm System, required the cooperative efforts of particle-board manufacturers, hardware manufacturers, machinery manufacturers, and cabinet manufacturers. This system has probably caused the biggest revolution in the cabinetmaking industry since the development of plywood.

Cabinetmaking, prior to the development of System 32, was a very labor-intensive operation and was not particularly efficient in its use of wood products. The frameless system has resulted in the redesigning of the basic construction of cabinets so that modern production machinery can be used to reduce the labor required to build cabinets. One of the major changes has been the elimination of the cabinet face frame, resulting in the elimination of a labor-intensive step in cabinet construction. The frameless system also elimi-nates most dado and rabbet joints, resulting in further labor savings. Material savings also come from the elimination of the face frame and from the fact that the frameless system is usually characterized by the use of laminated particle board as the major construction material rather than more expensive hardwood lumber and plywood.

THEORY OF THE FRAMELESS SYSTEM

The frameless cabinetmaking system involves the construction of a basic box. This box has no face frame as found in traditional cabinet construction. The boxes are usually made of 5/8-in. or 3/4-in. material with 1/4-in. backs.

Central to the frameless system are two vertical rows of holes in each vertical cabinet member (sides and partitions). These rows of holes (Figure 1-1), known as system holes or hardware holes, are used to locate and mount door hinge-mounting plates, drawer runners, and adjustable shelves. These holes are 5 mm in diameter and are 32 mm apart, center to center (thus the name *System 32*).

The mounting holes for all hinges and drawer runners are on 32-mm increments so they can be mounted using the system holes.

The cabinet boxes are most often assembled using wood dowels. This requires boring another series of holes, known as construction holes (Figure 1-2). These holes are oriented horizontally and are used to join cabinet ends

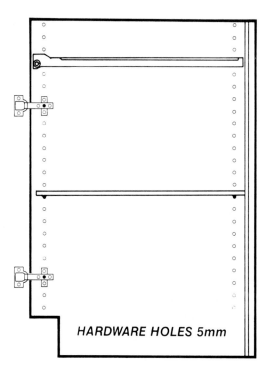

HARDWARE HOLES 5mm

Figure 1-1 System, or hardware, holes.(Courtesy of Julius Blum, Inc.)

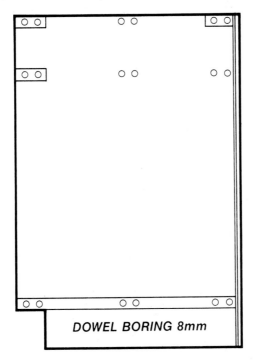

DOWEL BORING 8mm

Figure 1-2 Construction (dowel) holes. (Courtesy of Julius Blum, Inc.)

to cabinet bottoms and to attach stretcher rails to cabinet ends. Smaller shops, lacking a boring machine, may use a wafer plate-jointing system or may use screws for assembly.

Since the cabinets do not use face frames, the front edges of the cabinet box are exposed. These surfaces are covered with any one of a number of edge-banding materials. Edge banding is available to match the sheet material used to construct the cabinet box. Wood edge banding may also be used.

Special concealed hinges have been developed for mounting doors on the cabinet boxes. These hinges are used in conjunction with separate mounting plates. The hinge is attached to the door, and the mounting plate is attached to the side of the cabinet. The door is then installed by attaching the hinge to the mounting plate with a fixing screw. The doors are usually mounted so that they cover the front edge of the cabinet side. Even though the hinge is mounted inside the cabinet, its geometry allows the door to swing open without binding on the cabinet side or with a door mounted on an adjacent cabinet. These hinges allow the door to be adjusted in or out from the cabinet face as well as left to right and up or down.

Drawers are mounted on roller guides attached to the cabinet sides.

SYSTEM APPROACH

Frameless cabinetmaking is a system approach to cabinetmaking. The system consists of cabinet sheet materials, matching edge-banding materials, special hardware, special machines, and a method of constructing cabinets that takes advantage of the other parts of the system. The use of a computer to help design the cabinets, produce shop drawings, and generate cutting lists can greatly enhance the system.

There are several basic prerequisites to make this system work efficiently.

- Materials for the cabinet boxes must be flat, uniform in thickness, and stable, with little tendency to warp.
- Hardware must be designed to take advantage of the 32-mm system.
- Machinery must also be designed for this system. Saws must be capable of cutting sheet material to very close tolerances with no chipping.

Edge-banding machines are needed to apply edge banding to exposed edges. Boring machines are needed to accurately bore the system holes and construction holes (if used). Assembly equipment that will ensure that the cabinet boxes are assembled perfectly square is needed.

ADVANTAGES OF THE FRAMELESS SYSTEM

Compared with the traditional face-frame cabinet construction system, the frameless system offers the following advantages.

Material costs are usually less because of the extensive use of laminated particle boards in place of hardwoods and because of the elimination of the face frame. There is also less material waste because these materials can be cut without regard to grain direction. Labor costs are less because of the efficient construction system; the fact that conventional dado, rabbet, and miter joints are eliminated; and the fact that the labor-intensive face frame is eliminated. The frameless system lends itself to the construction of "knocked-down" (KD) or ready-to-assemble (RTA) cabinets that can easily be assembled on the job site. The system is versatile. It is possible to build sleek, clean, laminate-clad cabinets or traditional-appearing cabinets just by changing doors and drawer fronts and using wood panels on exposed cabinet ends.

The finishing operations are also greatly reduced. The laminated particle-board materials require no finishing, so the only finishing required, if any, is on wood trim such as door and drawer pulls and wood countertop edges.

A more detailed discussion of the frameless system is presented in Chapter 2.

THE PLACE OF TRADITIONAL FACE-FRAME CABINETS IN TODAY'S INDUSTRY

With all the advantages offered by the frameless system, one might reasonably ask why anyone would continue to build traditional face-frame cabinets. There is at least one good reason: Some customers still want them! Even though it is possible to achieve a traditional cabinet appearance with frameless cabinets by using frame-and-panel wood doors and matching drawer fronts, it is not quite the same. Many customers want the traditional appearance, with the spacing between doors and drawers and exposed hardware that face-frame construction provides.

It is also true that a substantial investment in equipment is required to become efficient in the frameless system. Some shops may not be able to make this investment. However, it will probably become increasingly difficult for shops to compete on a cost basis by continuing to use the traditional system. It will be necessary to charge more for traditional cabinets because of higher labor and material costs. It is true that many of the first shops to adopt the frameless system were charging more for frameless cabinets than for traditional cabinets. This was due partly to the fact that there was more demand than there was production capacity, and partly to the need to recoup initial equipment investment. In the long run it will be less expensive to build cabinets using the frameless system than the traditional system. Some shops have estimated that there is a labor savings of up to 50% using the frameless system compared with the traditional face-frame system.

Section Three of this book covers the traditional face-frame cabinetmaking system.

SECTION TWO

Construction
of Frameless Cabinets

The construction technique used for frameless cabinets is very different from the technique used for face-frame cabinets. The adoption of the frameless system almost always requires an investment in specialized equipment.

Section Two includes Chapters 5 to 9 and discusses the special construction techniques and equipment requirements for building frameless cabinets.

Chapter 5 covers panel cutting and discusses the equipment options. Chapter 6 covers the many options available for edge banding panels, and Chapter 7 covers boring system holes and construction holes. Chapter 8 covers cabinet assembly techniques, and Chapter 9 presents many options for door and drawer construction.

CHAPTER 2

Characteristics
of the Frameless System

The main difference between the frameless system and the traditional method of making cabinets is that there is no face frame on the frameless-style cabinets. Doors and drawers are mounted directly on the cabinet sides or partitions. Also unique to frameless cabinets is the fact that most of the critical cabinet dimensions are in multiples of 32 mm to take advantage of special hardware designed for the system.

The frameless system is also noted for its use of laminated particle-board sheet material, both for the cabinet boxes as well as for door and drawer fronts. Solid hardwood is usually limited to trim items. While it is true that most frameless cabinets use these materials, it is also possible to use wood-veneer plywoods and wood door and drawer fronts for a more traditional appearance while still utilizing the frameless system.

In any case, it is very important that the material used be flat, straight, square, and of uniform thickness. The entire system depends on being able to produce perfectly square cabinet boxes to very accurate dimensions. This cannot be done with warped or out-of-square material or material that varies in thickness.

THE USE OF SYSTEM HOLES

The core of the frameless system is the use of system holes, also known as hardware holes. The system holes consist of two vertical rows of holes on each cabinet end or partition (Figure 2-1).

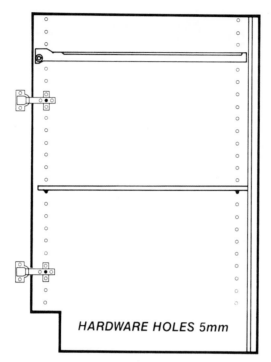

HARDWARE HOLES 5mm

Figure 2-1 System, or hardware, holes. (Courtesy of Julius Blum, Inc.)

These holes are 5 mm in diameter, usually 13 mm deep, and spaced on 32-mm increments measured from center to center. These holes are used to locate and attach hardware such as hinge-mounting plates, drawer guides, and adjustable shelf supports. This hardware is attached with short, thick screws designed for the 5-mm holes. These screws are known as system screws, or Euroscrews. The hinge-mounting plates, for example, are mounted with two screws located on 32-mm centers so they can be mounted using any two adjacent system holes.

The row of holes nearest the front of the cabinet is centered 37 mm from the front edge of the cabinet. The back row of holes is measured from the front row and will always be on some multiple of 32 mm. On a base cabinet this measurement is usually determined by the length of the drawer guide that is to be used, or more specifically, the distance between screw holes on the drawer guide. The distance between screw holes will always be a multiple of 32 mm.

A considerable labor savings can result from mounting hinge plates and drawer guides in the system holes before assembling the cabinet. This eliminates reaching inside the assembled cabinet to attach these items.

The distance between the back row of holes and the back of the cabinet is not particularly critical.

Determining cabinet height. A typical kitchen base cabinet is 36 in. high, including the thickness of the countertop. The height of a frameless base cabinet will usually be determined by the system hole-drilling pattern. There are two ways to establish cabinet heights.

The first system allows cabinet heights to be in multiples of 32 mm plus one thickness of the material being used. (The thickness of the countertop must then be added to get the final height of a base cabinet.) The holes are laid out as shown in Figure 2-2. The first hole will be bored at one-half the material thickness from the top of the cabinet (8 mm for 5/8-in. material or 9.5 mm for 3/4-in. material). The rest of the vertical row of holes is drilled on 32-mm centers, with the last hole again being located at one-half the material thickness from the bottom of the cabinet.

This system allows cabinet height to be varied in increments of 32 mm. The actual height of the cabinet box will be a multiple of 32 mm plus one material thickness. Note that the toe-kick area may be included as part of the cabinet end, as in Figure 2-2, or it may be added later.

The second method allows building cabinets of any height by providing an unspecified spacing between the bottom hole and the bottom of the

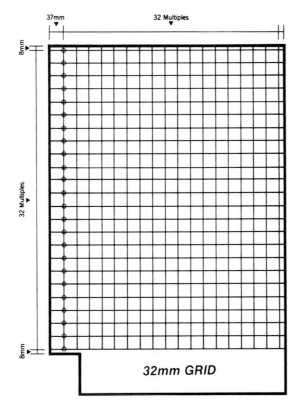

32mm GRID

Figure 2-2 System holes with 32-mm grid. (Courtesy of Julius Blum, Inc.)

cabinet. This unspecified distance is called float. The first hole is still indexed at one-half the material thickness from the top of the cabinet, and subsequent holes are spaced 32 mm center to center. This allows greater flexibility in cabinet height but keeps drawer spacing the same from the top of the base cabinets. It may, however, mean that a bottom drawer in a bank of drawers will have a height that is not a multiple of 32 mm. This float may be located at either the top or bottom of wall cabinets.

See Chapter 7 for a discussion of methods and equipment for drilling system holes.

THE USE OF CONSTRUCTION HOLES

Construction holes are used for dowel joint assembly of cabinet parts or for the use of some types of KD (knocked-down) fasteners. Most larger production shops and many smaller shops use dowel assembly, so they will need to drill construction holes. Some smaller shops use the wafer plate-jointing system for assembling cabinets. Others use special screws for assembly. In the latter two cases, construction holes will not be necessary.

Construction holes are 8 mm in diameter and are drilled in horizontal patterns, as shown in Figure 2-3. They should be as deep as possible for

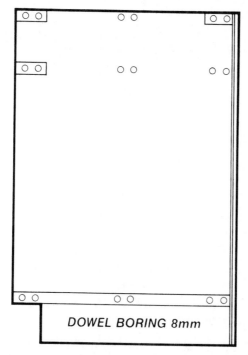

DOWEL BORING 8mm

Figure 2-3 Construction holes. (Courtesy of Julius Blum, Inc.)

maximum strength. Their depth is usually 2 mm less than the thickness of the panel. They are used to attach the cabinet bottom, top, and any stretchers to the cabinet ends.

The use of construction holes requires that a shop have a second boring machine or a multipurpose machine that can be used to bore both system holes and construction holes.

It should be noted that dados and rabbets are seldom, if ever, used to assemble frameless cabinets, regardless of which of the previously described systems is used. This represents a great savings in time as well as eliminates a potential source of error.

EDGE BANDING

Since frameless cabinets do not have a face frame to cover the front edges of the cabinet-box components, it is necessary to cover the raw edges of the laminated particle-board components with edge banding. There are a number of materials available for edge banding. These include wood, high-pressure plastic-laminate strips, or any of several plastic banding materials.

Wood edge banding may be either solid wood strips or thin veneer, available in rolls with or without a pregluing adhesive applied.

High-pressure plastic-laminate strips may be applied with contact cement or with one of the edge-banding machines described in Chapter 6. Of the plastic edge-banding materials, PVC is the most popular. It is used with automatic and semiautomatic edge-banding machines with hot-melt adhesives. Polyester edge banding is somewhat more expensive but can be used with preapplied heat-sensitive adhesive and applied with one of the benchtop banders with a heating platen or even with a hot iron.

The edge-banding manufacturers have gone to great effort to match plastic laminates and laminated particle boards from various manufacturers in both color and texture. Some of them publish cross-reference charts to assist in matching colors. Such a chart is shown in Figure 4-27.

Wood edge banding is used on plywood edges, but it is also used to provide a decorative effect with plastic laminates and laminated particle boards. Some shops edge-band plastic-laminate-faced doors and drawer fronts in wood (Figure 2-4).

Wood edge banding can be in the form of very thin veneer rolls and can be applied with automatic edge banders. These rolls of wood-veneer banding are also available preglued for use with small banders or for hot-iron applications.

Thick wood strips (1/8 in. to 3/4 in.) may also be used as edge banding. Some of the large commercial edge banders can apply thick wood edge banding automatically. Thick wood strips may be glued or nailed and glued.

Figure 2-4 Wood edge banding on doors and drawer fronts

The primary purpose of edge banding is to cover the edges of particle board or plywood cabinet components. However, the edge banding must be durable to resist damage from impact on the edge of the board. It must be securely attached so that it will not come off in service, and there must be no visible glue line.

Edge-banding systems and machines are described in more detail in Chapter 6.

HARDWARE

The frameless system could not work without special hardware. In fact, hardware manufacturers were very instrumental in developing the frameless system. The main frameless system hardware items are hinges and hinge-mounting plates, and drawer guides. However, there are many other useful hardware items that make the frameless cabinetmaking system easier. These include cabinet levelers with toe-kick attachments for base cabinets, hanging brackets for wall cabinets, adjustable drawer-front attachment systems, cover caps for screws and holes, and assembly fittings that allow cabinets to be shipped knocked down and then assembled on the job site.

Hinges and mounting plates.   Frameless cabinets are noted for the use of totally concealed hinges (Figure 2-5). Variations of this hinge and mounting plate allow the mounting of cabinet doors in full overlay, half overlay, or inset (flush) applications (Figure 2-6).

Full overlay is often used at the end of a cabinet whereas half overlay is used when there is a partition in a cabinet, with doors being mounted on both sides of the partition. The inset, or flush, application is not used as often but may be used if the designer wants the cabinet edges to form a visual border around the doors and drawer fronts. Sometimes a contrasting color or a wood edge banding is used to emphasize the effect.

Special hinges are available for extra-thick doors, for corner cabinets with 45°-angle fronts, for providing extra clearance for roll-out trays, and for mounting in corner cabinets where there is no cabinet end or partition to provide a mounting surface. Hinges are available in various opening angles from about 100° to over 170°.

Figure 2-5 Typical frameless hinge. (Courtesy of Julius Blum, Inc.)

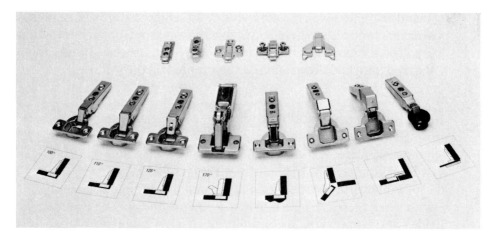

Figure 2-6 Full-overlay, half-overlay, and inset (flush) hinge applications. (Courtesy of Julius Blum, Inc.)

The hinge is first mounted to the door by boring a 35-mm hole for the hinge cup and then using two mounting screws. Also available are press-in hinges that have premounted nylon dowels attached to the hinge. The door is drilled with the 35-mm hole and two 8-mm holes to accept the nylon dowels (Figure 2-7). Machines are available to drill the 35-mm hole and the two 8-mm holes in one operation.

The hinge plate is mounted to the cabinet end or partition using two of the 5-mm system holes and two system (Euro) screws. The door is hung by sliding the hinges (which are already attached to the door) onto the mounting plate and tightening a single screw. The door can then be adjusted inward or

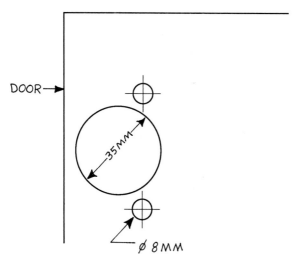

Figure 2-7 Door-boring pattern for a typical press-in hinge application

outward, from side to side, and upward or downward by adjusting various screws on the hinge.

Drawer guides.   Drawer guides are mounted on either the drawer side or on the bottom corners of the drawer. They may be either three-quarter extension or full extension. Most have an epoxy-coated finish to match the interior cabinet surfaces. These guides are shown in Figure 2-8.

Most side and bottom roller systems have a captive rail on one side that eliminates unnecessary side movement of the drawer, even if it is slightly undersize in relation to the drawer-opening width.

The bottom-mount guides have the additional advantage of supporting the drawer bottom so it can merely be butted to the underside of the drawer sides rather than having to be supported in a groove.

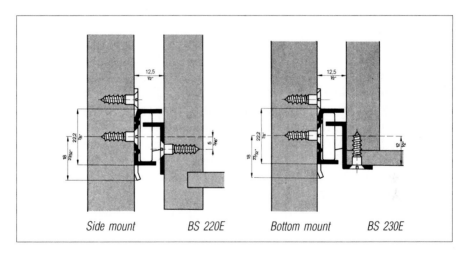

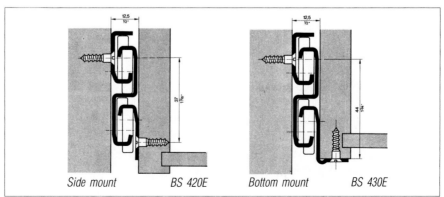

Figure 2-8 Bottom, side, and full-extension drawer guides. (Courtesy of Julius Blum, Inc.)

Drawer guides are attached to the drawers with wood screws and to the cabinet sides with system screws using the 5-mm system holes discussed earlier.

Shelf supports.   There are a variety of metal and plastic shelf supports available. They are all designed to plug into the 5-mm system holes.

KD fasteners.   KD fasteners are designed to allow cabinet parts to be shipped unassembled (knocked down) and then assembled on the job site. This system is also known as RTA (ready-to-assemble). This can result in a considerable savings in packaging and shipping costs because the bulk of the cabinet is greatly reduced. The hardware manufacturers have devised a number of clever systems to accomplish this. For a more detailed discussion of these systems and other hardware items, see Chapter 4.

ASSEMBLY

When using the frameless system, it is very important that cabinets be assembled so that they are perfectly square. Larger shops using dowel construction will probably use pneumatic case clamps that virtually guarantee squareness (assuming that the cabinet parts were accurately cut).

Smaller shops may use bar or pipe clamps. These can be used successfully, but great care must be taken to apply uniform pressure along the joint and to make sure that the cabinet is square. Care must also be taken to avoid damaging the cabinet surfaces.

If screws are used for assembly, the cabinet is usually clamped together while the screws are installed. An alternative to clamping is to use KD (or RTA) assembly fasteners to assemble the cabinets.

A more detailed discussion of assembly systems and equipment is presented in Chapter 8.

CONSTRUCTION DETAILS

There are three major types of cabinets that we will be concerned with. These are the base cabinet, the wall cabinet, and the tall utility cabinet. In each case, the component parts are joined with butt joints that are reinforced with either dowels, wood wafer plates, or screws.

Base cabinets.   The box for a base cabinet usually consists of two ends, a bottom, a back, and some stretchers. There may also be interior partitions. The cabinet base that provides the toe-kick space may be an integral part of the cabinet or it may be a separate structure.

The end for a typical base cabinet with an integral toe-kick base is shown in Figure 2-9. The example shown is designed for dowel construction. The location of the bottom, stretchers, and back would be the same for the other fastening systems.

A typical end for a cabinet with a nonintegral toe-kick base is shown in Figure 2-10. An assembled cabinet without doors, drawers, or adjustable shelves is shown in Figure 2-11. It should be noted that it is not always necessary to have the bottom stretcher shown in these illustrations.

Cabinet leveler legs (Figure 2-12) have become very popular on frameless cabinets. They are attached to the underside of the cabinet in lieu of a

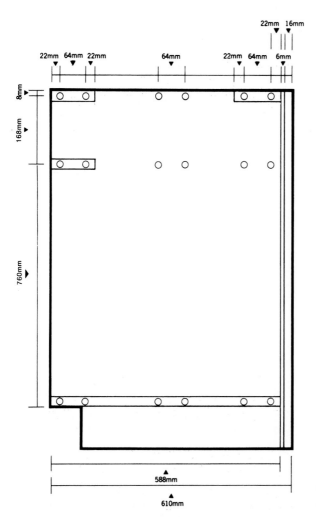

Figure 2-9 Base-cabinet end showing drilling pattern. (Courtesy of Julius Blum, Inc.)

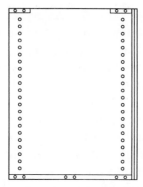

Figure 2-10 Base-cabinet end without an integral toe kick

base assembly. When the cabinet is installed, these legs can easily be adjusted to level the cabinet. The toe-kick board is then attached by snapping it to the leg leveler with a special fitting (Figure 2-13). The toe-kick board can easily be removed for cleaning under the cabinet.

Corner base cabinets.   Corner cabinets always present a challenge to obtaining good space utilization. Three common corner-cabinet arrange-

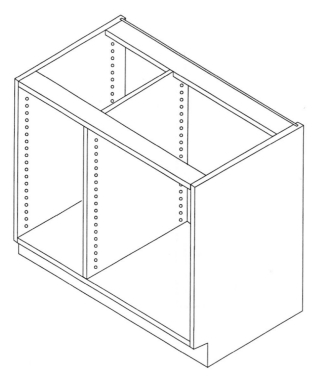

Figure 2-11 Assembled base-cabinet box

Figure 2-12 Cabinet leveler legs. (Courtesy of Julius Blum, Inc.)

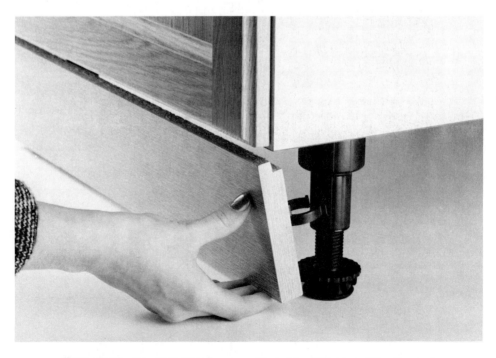

Figure 2-13 Toe-kick clips for use with cabinet levelers. (Courtesy of Julius Blum, Inc.)

ments are shown in Figure 2-14. The corner cabinet shown in Figure 2-14(a) has the front angled 45° with the other cabinets and usually features revolving (Lazy Susan) shelves. The top stretchers are replaced by a solid top panel. Special hinges are available for mounting doors on this type of cabinet (Figure 2-15).

The corner-cabinet arrangement shown in Figure 2-14(b) does not provide as easy access to the contents of the corner cabinet as the previous one does, but it is easy to construct and is often used where space is not critical.

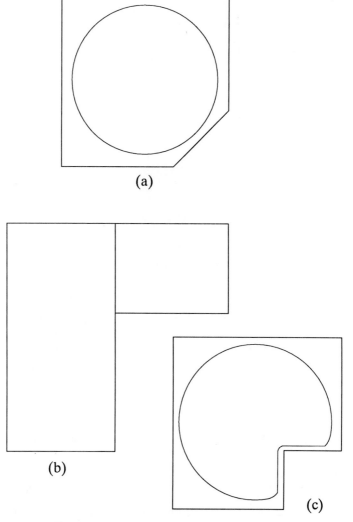

(a)

(b)

(c)

Figure 2-14   Corner-cabinet arrangements

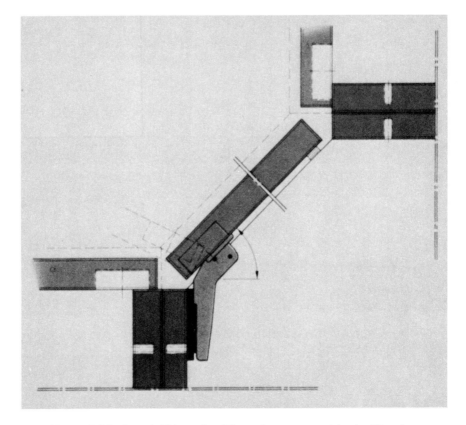

Figure 2-15 Special hinge for 45°-angle corner cabinets. (Courtesy of Mepla Inc., Furniture Fittings)

This arrangement consists of one cabinet that extends into the corner of the room and another cabinet that butts against it. There are also special hinges available for this application (Figure 2-16).

The third corner cabinet, shown in Figure 2-14(c), is not used as often as the other two but does have some advantages. It is used with precut revolving trays. The door is usually designed so that it also hinges in the center in order to fold back against itself when open.

Wall cabinets.   The construction of the wall cabinet is quite similar to the base cabinet except that there is no base to be concerned with, and a solid panel top is used rather than stretcher rails. A typical wall-cabinet end is shown in Figure 2-17. It is worth noting that left- and right-hand cabinet ends can be interchangeable if cabinet heights are in multiples of 32 mm plus one material thickness. The boring must be accurate, but this can save setup time in making

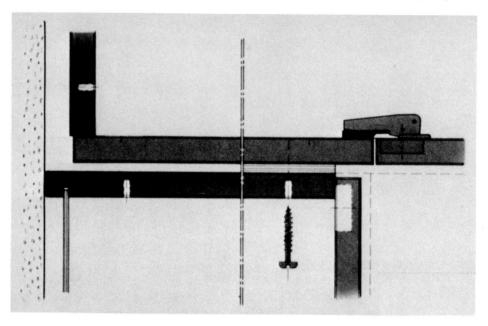

Figure 2-16 Special hinge for 90°-angle corner cabinets. (Courtesy of Mepla Inc., Furniture Fittings)

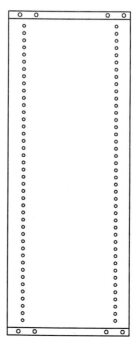

Figure 2-17 Typical wall-cabinet end

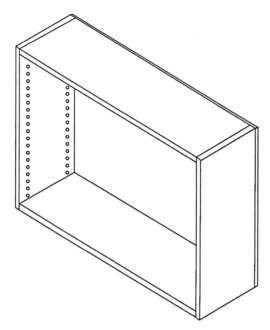

Figure 2-18 Typical wall-cabinet box

separate right- and left-hand ends. A typical wall cabinet minus doors and shelves is shown in Figure 2-18.

The hardware manufacturers make some special hardware for attaching wall cabinets to the wall. The use of this hardware will usually require notching the cabinet ends, backs, or both. This hardware is described in Chapter 4.

Tall utility cabinets.   Tall utility cabinets can be used to house appliances such as conventional or microwave ovens, or they can be used for food storage or even as a broom closet. They can be equipped with pull-out trays or shelves and door-mounted trays.

The tall utility cabinet is built much the same as a base cabinet except for the extra height. The main differences are that a solid panel top replaces the top stretcher rails and if adjustable shelves are used, a fixed shelf is used at mid-cabinet height to stiffen the cabinet sides. A typical tall utility cabinet is shown in Figure 2-19.

Figures 2-20 through 2-22 show exploded views of typical base, wall, and utility cabinets, along with some of the available hardware and assembly connection systems.

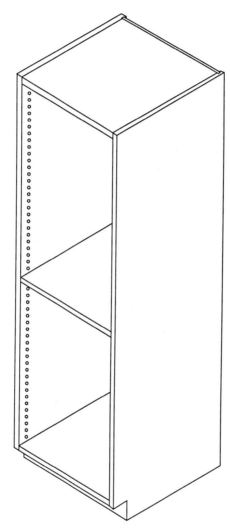

Figure 2-19   Typical tall utility cabinet

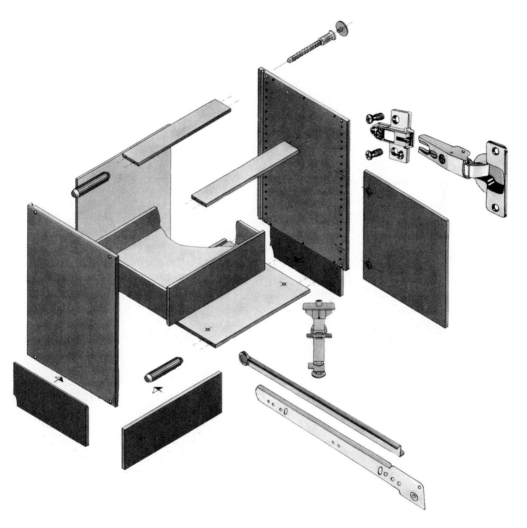

Figure 2-20 Exploded view of a typical base cabinet. (Courtesy of Mepla Inc., Furniture Fittings)

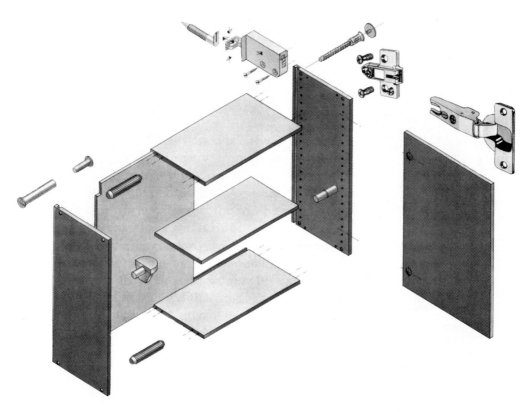

Figure 2-21 Exploded view of a typical wall cabinet. (Courtesy of Mepla Inc., Furniture Fittings)

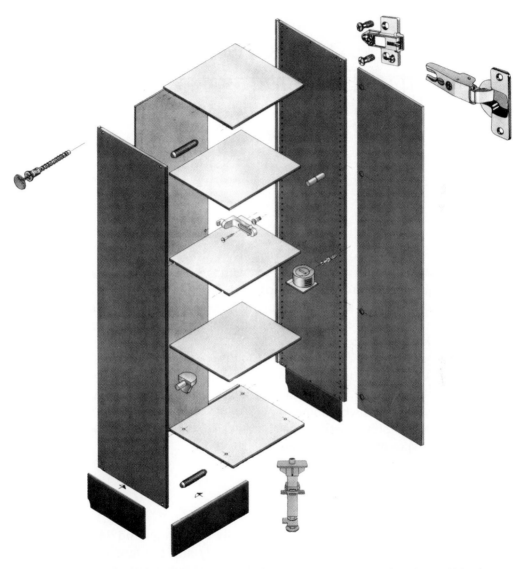

Figure 2-22 Exploded view of a typical utility cabinet. (Courtesy of Mepla Inc., Furniture Fittings)

CHAPTER 3

Characteristics
of the Face-Frame System

Despite the popularity and many advantages of the frameless system, there remains a strong market for face-frame cabinets. While it is possible to give frameless cabinets a traditional appearance by using frame-and-panel doors and matching drawer fronts, it isn't quite the same as the effect achieved with face-frame cabinets.

There is also some concern about the strength of frameless cabinets. It is true that a well-made face frame contributes strength to the cabinet, but if the frameless cabinet is designed properly, it will not need the extra strength contributed by a face frame.

This chapter examines the characteristics and construction details of the various types of face-frame cabinets.

BASE CABINETS

Base cabinets for kitchen use are usually 36 in. high and 24 in. deep. They consist of two basic parts: the cabinet body and the face frame. The body consists of the cabinet ends, bottom, back, and any partitions or shelves. (The top is added after the cabinets are installed.) The cabinet ends are either finished ends or wall ends, depending on whether they show in the finished product. Finished ends are usually cut from a hardwood plywood to match the rest of the cabinet and are often cut so that they extend slightly beyond the cabinet back in order to be fitted to a slightly irregular wall. This extension is referred to as a "scribe," as it allows the contour of the wall to be marked or scribed on the cabinet end so that it may be cut or planed to fit the wall. The finished end also has a notch cut from the lower front corner to form the toe space. A nailing strip is placed along the back of the cabinet at the top for installation purposes (Figure 3-1).

Most of the joints on the base cabinets are butt joints assembled with glue and nails or staples. More complex joints are usually not required because base cabinets sit on the floor and the stresses are distributed over a large area. However, if heavy usage is anticipated, it is advisable to use dado and rabbet joints for joining the components. The cabinet back is always rabbeted into finished ends.

Partitions are used to divide various areas within a large cabinet and to support shelves. Partitions are usually used to separate a bank of drawers from the rest of a cabinet, as shown in Figure 3-1. Shelves in base cabinets are quite often fixed at a standard height, usually 11 in. from the bottom of the cabinet. However, space utilization is enhanced by making the shelves adjustable.

Roll-out trays are sometimes used in place of shelves to provide easy access to items in the cabinet. These are similar to drawers in construction and will be discussed in Chapter 12.

The face frame is a very important part of the cabinet. It defines the drawer and door openings and is the mounting surface for door hinges and for some types of drawer guides. It is visible on many types of cabinets and is usually made from a hardwood matching the rest of the cabinet.

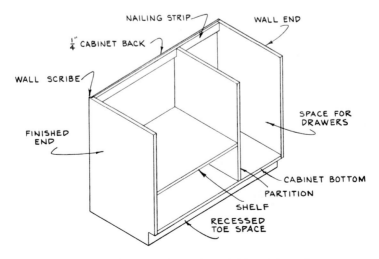

Figure 3-1 Base cabinet shown without face frame

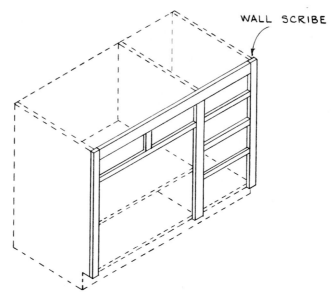

Figure 3-2 Base cabinet with face frame

If one end of the cabinet is to fit against a wall, the face frame is made slightly longer than the cabinet so that it may be scribed to fit the contour of the wall (Figure 3-2).

The vertical face-frame members on the extreme left and right of the frame are called stiles, and the horizontal pieces are called rails. Vertical members that run between the rails are called mullions (Figure 3-3).

These face-frame members are usually joined in one of three methods, depending on the equipment available in the shop. The strongest method is a mortise-and-tenon joint. This method does require a mortiser and preferably a tenoner as well (Figure 3-4).

Another joining method often used in the smaller shop is butt joints with

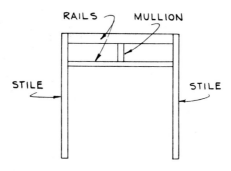

Figure 3-3 Face-frame components

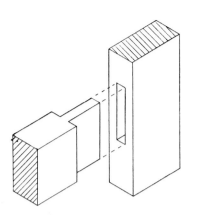

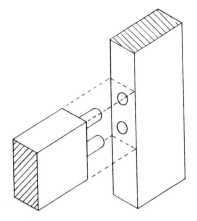

Figure 3-4 Mortise and tenon   **Figure 3-5** Butt joint with dowels

dowels (Figure 3-5). The equipment required ranges from simple hand-dow-eling jigs to multispindle boring machines.

A third method of joining face-frame members is to butt the pieces together and drive screws through the joint (Figure 3-6). This requires semi-automated equipment to clamp the frame members together, drill the holes at the proper angles, and install the screws.

Of the three methods, doweling probably requires the least equipment investment. It is important that face-frame members be securely joined. The constant opening and closing of doors, especially those with self-closing hinges, places a considerable load on the joint. The resulting movement between these parts will eventually cause the finish film to crack at the joint if the parts are not properly joined.

The face frame is glued and assembled as a unit before being attached to the cabinet body.

There are a few other face-frame details worth mentioning at this point. Notice that in all the face-frame illustrations, there are no horizontal bottom rails. This eliminates the need to lift objects over a rail when removing them from the bottom shelf; it makes the bottom shelf easier to clean; and it eliminates one extra step in construction. The front edge of the cabinet bottom is merely covered with an edge-banding strip. The doors extend to

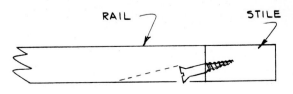

Figure 3-6 Butt joint with screws

the bottom of the face-frame rails and thus cover the front edge of the bottom.

It is not necessary to have a mullion between a pair of doors if the doors are fairly narrow (approximately 18 in. wide or narrower). Thus, it is possible to have an opening up to 36 in. wide without a face-frame member to obstruct access to the cabinet (Figure 3-7).

The sizes of face-frame parts will vary somewhat, depending on the type of doors and drawer fronts used (see Chapters 11 and 12), but in general they should not be any wider than necessary. Any unnecessary width of face-frame members encroaches on drawer space and access to cabinet shelf space. The following dimensions are adequate for face-frame members when lip doors and drawers are used. Other types of doors may require more room for mounting hinges. Stiles and mullions are usually 2 in. wide. (Stiles on finished ends are sometimes 1 1/2 in. wide because less of their surface is covered by doors.) Top rails are usually 2 1/2 in. wide to allow room for a pull board. Rails between drawers are usually 1 in. wide (Figure 3-8).

Figure 3-7   There is no mullion between the pair of doors on the right side of this cabinet.

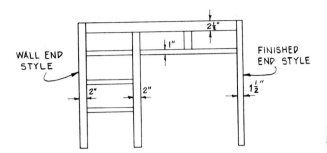

Figure 3-8 Typical face-frame-component sizes

The face frame for a sink cabinet is made as though there were going to be a drawer and doors under the sink. A false drawer front is attached in the drawer opening, or false-front trays, as shown in Figure 3-9, may be installed. Cabinets for surface cooking units (countertop ranges) are similar to the sink cabinet in construction.

A built-in oven requires a special cabinet that extends from the floor to the top of the wall cabinets, with an opening for the oven unit. This cabinet may have doors and a drawer below the oven unit and doors above it. It is usually 25 to 25 1/2 in. deep so that adjacent countertops will not extend beyond the front of this cabinet (Figure 3-10).

Figure 3-9 False-front trays used on a sink cabinet. (Courtesy of Amerock Corporation)

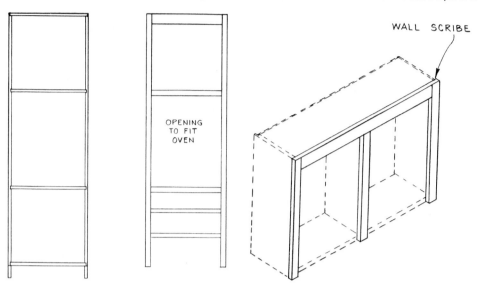

Figure 3-10 Typical oven cabinet and face frame

Figure 3-11 Wall-cabinet face frame

Built-in oven units vary in size, so specifications must be obtained from the manufacturer before the cabinet is designed. If the oven cabinet is floor-to-ceiling, the base must be left loose so that the cabinet can be set in place, lifted, and have the base slipped underneath.

WALL CABINETS

Wall cabinets are usually 12 in. deep and 30 to 36 in. high. Like the base cabinets, they also consist of a body and a face frame. However, the stress loadings on the joints are higher for a cabinet hanging on the wall than they are for one sitting on the floor. Therefore, the structural parts are almost always jointed with rabbet or dado joints.

The wall-cabinet face frame is very similar to that of the base cabinet except that the top rail may be somewhat wider, especially if the cabinets extend to the ceiling. As on the base cabinet, the face frame extends 1/2 in. beyond the end of the cabinet on wall ends so that it may be fitted tightly to the wall (Figure 3-11).

The wall-cabinet body is somewhat more complex than that of the base cabinet. Figure 3-12 shows the joinery involved in making the body for a wall cabinet with a finished left end, a wall end on the right, and a partition in the center.

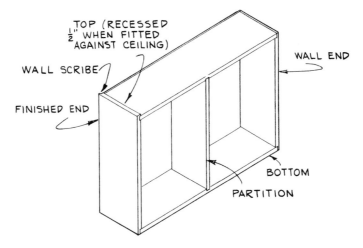

Figure 3-12 Wall-cabinet joinery

A nailing strip is also included in the wall cabinet for attaching the cabinet to the wall.

Wall cabinets above a range are designed to house an exhaust hood that may be 30 in. or 36 in. wide. The joinery for this cabinet is shown in Figure 3-13. Note that the partitions on either side of the exhaust hood are exposed below the hood and must be machined as finished ends. The center section of this cabinet has the bottom set about 12 in. higher than the bottom of the remainder of the cabinet to accommodate the exhaust hood.

The space left for a refrigerator is usually 36 in. wide by 72 in. high. A special cabinet 36 in. wide and 12 to 18 in. high may be built to go over the

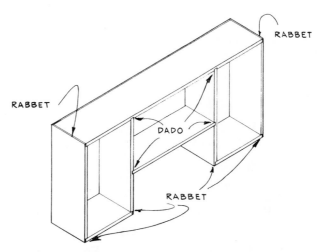

Figure 3-13 Wall cabinet to accommodate range exhaust hood

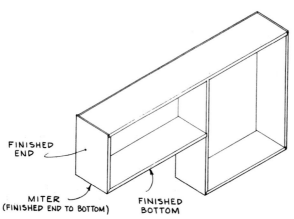

FINISHED
END

MITER
(FINISHED END TO BOTTOM)

FINISHED
BOTTOM

Figure 3-14 Refrigerator-cabinet construction

refrigerator, or a larger cabinet may be designed to fit beside and above the refrigerator (Figure 3-14).

The bottom surface of a cabinet directly above the refrigerator is somewhat visible and is usually made from the same material as finished ends. It would, in that case, be mitered to the finished end, as in Figure 3-14.

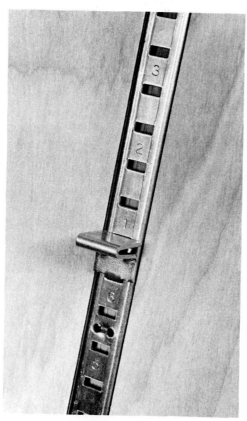

Figure 3-15 Adjustable shelf standard and clip

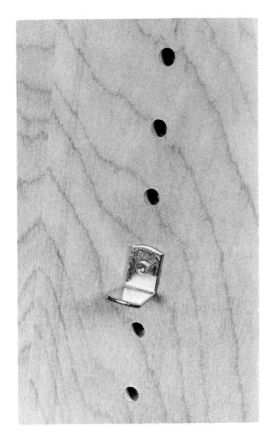

Figure 3-16 Adjustable shelf support

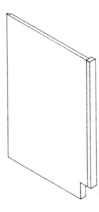

Figure 3-17 Dishwasher end

Wall cabinets are usually fitted with adjustable shelves. These shelves are supported by clips that attach to a metal shelf standard, as shown in Figure 3-15, or they may be supported by clips that are inserted into 1/4-in.-diameter holes drilled in the cabinet walls or partitions, as shown in Figure 3-16.

SPECIAL CABINETS

A built-in dishwasher requires no special cabinet. It requires only an opening between base cabinets (usually 24 1/2 in.). The countertop extends over the top of the dishwasher. If the dishwasher is located at the end of a base cabinet and would have an exposed end, a special dishwasher end is made that is very

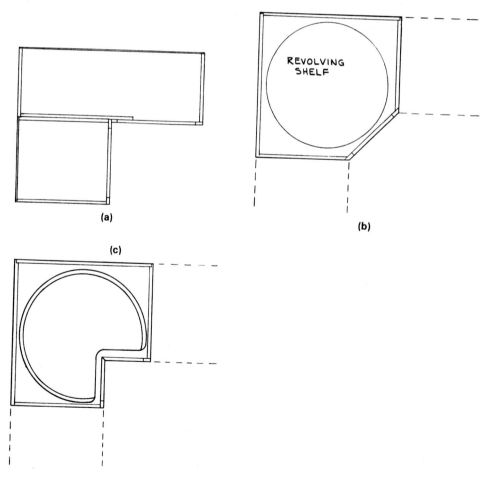

REVOLVING
SHELF

(a)

(b)

(c)

Figure 3-18   Three types of corner cabinets

similar to a finished end on a cabinet (Figure 3-17). The dishwasher end supports the countertop and is nailed to the floor at its base.

Corner cabinets present a special problem in space utilization, and there are no easy answers. Figure 3-18 shows three types of corner cabinets.

The L-shaped cabinet shown in Figure 3-18(a) is actually two cabinets, one of which is placed in the corner and the other then merely butted against it to form the corner. This is the most common and least expensive method because standard cabinet construction is used. It is difficult, however, to reach and remove items stored in the corner area, so this storage must be considered only for seldom-used items. This type is acceptable when cabinet space is plentiful.

If this type of cabinet extends into the room to form an eating bar, a door may be placed on the back of the cabinet to provide access to the corner, thus solving the problem.

For kitchens with limited cabinet space, it is usually worth the expense to use corner cabinets such as the ones shown in Figure 3-18(b) and (c). Corner cabinet B is more difficult to construct than A because of the angles involved and because it does not utilize standard cabinet sheet materials as efficiently. It does, however, provide somewhat easier access to items stored in the corner and can utilize revolving Lazy Susan shelves. It does encroach slightly on room floor space, and it makes reaching the top shelves of the wall cabinet above more difficult.

The Lazy Susan cabinet shown in Figure 3-18(c) provides easy access to items stored in the corner, but it requires extra time and hardware in its con-

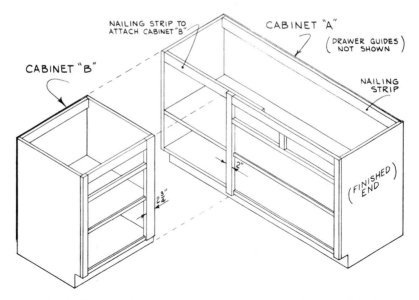

Figure 3-19 Typical method of joining corner base cabinets

CABINET "B"   CABINET "A"

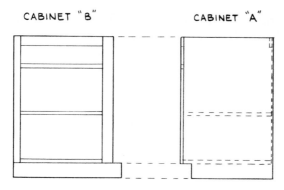

Figure 3-20 Corner-cabinet construction. The toe-kick board on cabinet "B" is extended to fit the toe space of cabinet "A."

struction. Some such cabinets are built with the door attached directly to the Lazy Susan shelves so that it revolves with the shelves. However, it is difficult, if not impossible, to make this door match the rest of the cabinet doors. Others utilize a hinged L-shaped door. Special hardware must be used so that the revolving shelf unit stops in the proper location for the door to close.

Figure 3-19 shows construction details of the corner cabinet shown in Figure 3-18(a). Construction is similar to any other base cabinet except for the face frame.

Notice that the face frame on cabinet A stops where it will meet cabinet B. The left stile on cabinet A is 2 in. wide, as usual. The right stile on cabinet B is 2 3/4 in. wide because it extends past the end of the face frame on cabinet A.

It is also necessary to extend the toe-kick board on cabinet B to meet the one on cabinet A (Figure 3-20).

BATH CABINETS

Bath vanity cabinets are similar in construction to kitchen base cabinets, with a few minor exceptions. They are usually only 32 in. high, rather than 36 in. They are usually 20 to 22 in. deep, rather than 24 in. If a one-piece cast countertop lavatory is to be used, its dimensions must be obtained and the cabinet built to fit.

The base cabinet will usually have doors under the lavatory area and a bank of drawers on one side if space permits.

CHAPTER 4

Cabinet Materials

Conventional face-frame cabinets have traditionally been built primarily of wood, plywood, and particle board, with most exterior surfaces being hardwood or hardwood-veneered plywood. Frameless cabinets are usually built of particle board with exposed surfaces covered with high-pressure plastic laminate and interior surfaces covered with polyester, melamine, or vinyl laminates or other coverings. However, the exterior surfaces of frameless cabinets can be made of hardwoods and, conversely, the interior surfaces of traditional face-frame cabinets can be made from any of the laminated particle boards usually associated with frameless construction.

This chapter begins with a discussion of wood as a material and then covers other materials used in frameless and traditional cabinet construction.

Wood offers many advantages to the cabinetmaker. It is easy to cut and machine with general-purpose machines. In other words, it is not necessary to invest in sophisticated, special-purpose machines to produce wood parts. It is relatively easy to join parts, either with mechanical fasteners or adhesives. Wood is also relatively easy to finish.

In spite of all these advantages, wood is not without its problems. It is subject to shrinkage, swelling, warping, and checking when subjected to different humidity levels. Not only do boards shrink as they dry, but they also shrink at different rates along each of their major axes (thickness, width, and length). Wood is also subject to a number of natural defects or limitations, such as knots, pitch pockets, and internal stresses. Woods of the same species

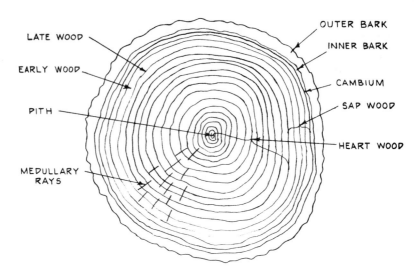

Figure 4-1 Tree cross section

may vary considerably in color and grain pattern, requiring selective matching in cabinet work. An understanding of the structure of wood is very helpful in solving these problems. A discussion of the composition and some of the properties of wood follows.

CLASSIFICATION OF TREES

Commercially useful woods are classified as softwoods if they are from coniferous trees and as hardwoods if they are from deciduous trees. Coniferous, or cone-bearing, trees are evergreens and include such trees as Douglas fir, hemlock, the pines, and the cedars. Deciduous trees are broad-leafed trees that lose their leaves in winter and include such trees as the oaks, walnut, maple, and cherry. This may seem like a rather arbitrary system of classification, since some hardwoods are softer than some softwoods. However, there are some important differences in the wood structure of the two types. And though there are a number of exceptions, it is generally true that the wood from deciduous trees is harder than that from coniferous trees.

WOOD COMPOSITION

Wood is made up of many small cells. Tree growth occurs by cell division. The wood cells are formed in the cambium, a very thin layer, one cell thick, between the wood and the bark. Most of these cells are long and tubular and have pointed ends. They are cemented together with a substance known as lignin. Most of these cells are oriented vertically in the tree.

Examination of the cross section of a tree trunk shows the following features (Figure 4-1).

Bark.   The new bark cells are also formed in the cambium layer, so the bark growth actually occurs from inside the tree. This new bark growth is known as the inner bark. The outer bark is formed as cells from the inner bark become dead or inactive. It is quite brittle and unable to stretch as the tree grows, so it cracks and eventually sloughs off. It does provide the tree with protection against insects and diseases. The cambium is the area in which this new growth occurs. Both bark and wood cells are formed in the cambium.

Sapwood.   The wood cells formed in the cambium layer become sapwood, the lighter-colored wood near the bark. These cells are active in conducting and storing sap for the tree and are considered to be the living part of the wood.

Heartwood.   The darker center area of the tree is known as the heartwood. It is made up of cells that are technically dead or no longer active in the life process of the tree. The darker color is caused by resins, tannins, and other chemical materials deposited in the cells.

Although the sapwood has most of the same strength properties as the heartwood, it is usually less desirable as a cabinet wood because of its lack of coloring. The colors that we usually associate with the fine cabinet and furniture woods are the heartwood colors. For example, the sapwood of black walnut wood is a very light yellow brown rather than the desirable rich brown of the heartwood. The heartwood is also more resistant to decay because of the resin deposits.

Pith.   The pith is the center of the trunk. It is rather soft and pronounced in some trees, and almost invisible in others.

Growth rings.   The wood cells formed early in each growing season are relatively large and have thin walls, resulting in a relatively soft wood known as earlywood or springwood. As the growth rate slows later in the summer, the cells formed are smaller and the cell walls thicker. This results in a harder, denser wood known as latewood or summerwood. This darker ring of summer wood is known as the growth ring. The growth rings can be counted to find the age of the tree. The rings are usually most pronounced in trees that are grown in climates with distinct growing seasons. Wood grown in more temperate climates has growth rings, but they are very difficult to see. Growth rings form the characteristic grain patterns seen in all woods.

Medullary rays.   The medullary rays are cells that are oriented horizontally in the tree and serve the purpose of conducting food laterally in the tree. They radiate from the center of the tree and exist in all woods. In softwoods, these rays are only one cell thick and are visible only with very high magnification. On the other hand, many hardwoods such as oak have very prominent rays, which provide the wood with some of its characteristic markings. These rays are especially noticeable as large flecks on a radial cut as shown in Figure 4-2.

Microscopic features of wood.   Other important features of wood require magnification for study. An end-grain surface of a hardwood has many small openings known as pores or vessels. These pores are visible without magnification on some woods such as red oak. In some woods, these pores are larger in the springwood and appear to follow the growth ring. Such woods are known as ring-porous. Woods that have pores more uniformly distributed are known as diffuse-porous. This factor is useful in identifying certain woods.

There are several types of wood cells, but most of them are long, thin, tubular structures with pointed ends. Figure 4-3 shows a cross section of a group of wood cells.

The cell walls are made up of very small strands called microfibrils. These microfibrils are the smallest visible wood element and require the most powerful magnification in order to be seen. The microfibrils are made of cellulose, the basic wood substance, and lignin, an adhesivelike substance.

The lumen, or cell cavity, may contain water or some of the chemical materials mentioned earlier.

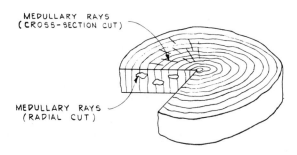

MEDULLARY RAYS
(CROSS-SECTION CUT)

MEDULLARY RAYS
(RADIAL CUT)

Figure 4-2 Medullary rays

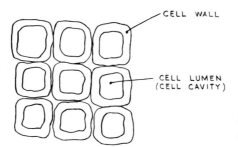

CELL WALL

CELL LUMEN
(CELL CAVITY)

Figure 4-3 Cross section of a group of wood cells

MOISTURE, SHRINKAGE, AND EXPANSION

One of the major problems faced by people building wood cabinets is that wood is not a dimensionally stable material. If a wood product is placed in a very dry environment, it will shrink. If it is placed back in a humid environment, it will expand. To compound the problem, a wood board will shrink and expand at very different rates along its three axes (thickness, width, length) depending upon how it was cut from the log. Some of the problems that are caused, at least in part, by moisture are warping, checking, cracking, and joint failure due to expansion and contraction.

Wood is a hygroscopic material in that it readily absorbs moisture in liquid and vapor form. It may actually absorb in excess of twice its weight in water. The amount of water in the wood is referred to as moisture content and is expressed as a percentage of the oven-dry weight of the wood sample. Thus, a board that weighed 2 lb. before being completely dried in an oven to a dry weight of 1 lb. would have had a moisture content of 100%. A board that weighed 1 1/2 lb. wet and 1 lb. dry would have had a 50% moisture content, and so forth. Moisture meters (Figure 4-4) are available for checking moisture content. The moisture content of a sample piece of wood may also be found by weighing it accurately and then drying it in an oven at 200° F until it stops losing weight, weighing it again, and applying the following formula:

$$\text{Moisture content (\%)} = \frac{\text{Wet weight} - \text{Oven-dry weight}}{\text{Oven-dry weight}} \times 100$$

The ideal moisture content for cabinet woods varies somewhat from one region of the country to another, depending on relative humidity, but usually it is between 6% and 8%. Wood should be dried to 6% to 7% for dry regions and 8% to 9% for humid regions.

When a dry sample of wood is placed in a humid environment, it quickly begins to absorb moisture. The first water to enter the wood is absorbed in the cell walls. This absorption causes the microfibril strands to expand. Eventually a point is reached where the cell wall is completely saturated and any

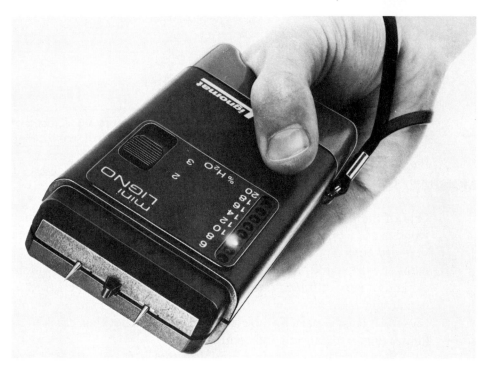

Figure 4-4   Wood moisture meter. (Courtesy of Lignomat USA, Ltd.)

additional water entering the cell is taken into the lumen or cell cavity. This is known as the *fiber saturation point;* it occurs at about 25% to 30% moisture content in most woods.

The water absorbed in the cell walls is known as *bound water*, and the water stored in the cell cavities is known as *free water*. Once the fiber saturation point is reached, maximum cell expansion has occurred, and the addition of more water will make the sample heavier but will not cause additional expansion. This sequence is reversed in drying lumber. When wood is dried from the wet, or "green," condition, the free water leaves first. After the free water is gone, the bound water in the cell walls is given up. Cell shrinkage starts when the wood is dried below the fiber saturation point. In theory, we could have a board with 100% moisture content and dry it to 30% moisture content (just above the fiber saturation point) with no shrinkage. However, in practice, this seldom happens because moisture travels through the board slowly; the moisture content of cells near the surface of the board may be well below the fiber saturation point while cells in the center are well over 30% moisture content. This brings up another problem. Moisture moves much faster along the grain than it does across the grain because of the tubular cell structure. Therefore, the ends of a board, if not sealed, will dry much faster than the center of the board. The rapid shrinkage of these cells relative to the

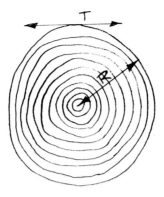

Figure 4-5 Tangential (T) direction versus radial (R) direction

cells in the center of the board causes the familiar cracks and checks often seen at the ends of boards.

Wood cells shrink very little in length, but they shrink considerably in diameter. Consequently, the lengthwise shrinkage of most boards is negligible, but the shrinkage in thickness and width must be taken into account. There is also a significant difference in the shrinkage rate in a radial direction (perpendicular to the growth rings) as compared with a tangential direction (tangent to the growth of rings). Figure 4-5 illustrates this.

Radial shrinkage ranges from 2% to 6% for various woods dried to 6% moisture content, and the tangential shrinkage will be about twice that value. Thus, if we compare two boards of the same width (Figure 4-6), board A, which is cut tangentially from the tree, will shrink twice as much in width as board B, which is cut radially.

Also, board A will tend to cup away from the center of the tree, as shown in Figure 4-7.

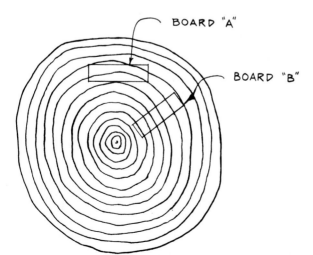

Figure 4-6 Tangential versus radial shrinkage. Board "A" will shrink approximately twice as much in width as board "B."

Figure 4-7 Normal tendency of a board to cup away from the center of the tree

Since the shrinkage rate is different along the grain than across it, any major deviation in grain direction, such as that found around a knot, will tend to make a board bow or warp as it shrinks.

So far we have painted a rather gloomy picture of the problems that may be expected when working with wood. However, everyone who has worked with wood has had to face the same problems, and a number of techniques have been developed to eliminate many of these problems.

Storing and handling wood.   One important consideration is to make sure that the moisture content of the wood has stabilized before you start working with it. If you started working the wood at 9% moisture content and it then dried to 7% moisture content, you would almost certainly have problems with warping and possibly checking. If you are building cabinets for a house in a relatively dry geographic area, for example, the moisture content of the wood should be 6% to 7%.

Wood should not be laid directly on the floor, where it can draw moisture. It should be stacked flat and well supported so that it is not allowed to sag or twist. Boards should not be leaned against an outside wall during the winter as there is a chance of drawing moisture.

Working with wood.   When working with solid lumber, a number of techniques may be used to prevent warpage. When gluing boards to make wide surfaces, it is best to cut the boards into narrow widths (1 1/2 to 3 in.) and glue these rather than glue wide boards. The growth rings should be alternated, as shown in Figure 4-8.

Any wide laminated wood surfaces should be attached to the final structure in a way that will allow them to expand and contract. Thus, a tabletop should be attached to the rails with blocks of wood as shown in Figure 4-9 rather than glued solidly in place. The panel in a frame-and-panel door should not be glued solidly in the frame but should only have a small spot of glue in the center, as shown in Figure 4-10, to hold it in place. This will allow the panel to expand without breaking the frame joints.

Figure 4-8 Direction of growth rings should be alternated when edge-gluing boards.

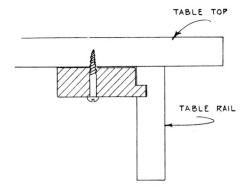

Figure 4-9 Method of attaching a tabletop to allow for expansion and contraction

Drawer bottoms made of solid wood should not be glued in place for the same reasons.

Applying a finish to the wood will retard the rate at which wood absorbs and loses moisture but will not totally prevent it. All surfaces, including unexposed areas, should be finished on solid wood to prevent an uneven rate of moisture change. For example, a tabletop that is finished only on the top surface will absorb moisture rapidly through the bottom surface and will tend to warp.

Shrinkage and swelling are not the only problems caused by the moisture content of wood. The strength of wood increases as it is dried below the fiber saturation point. Nail and screw holding power is also increased. Successful wood gluing and finishing both require low moisture levels in the wood. Also, wood that is above 20% moisture content is subject to attack by fungi.

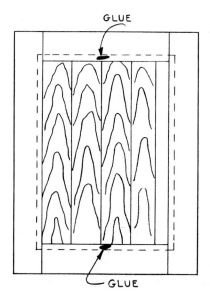

Figure 4-10 Glue applied to the center of a door panel to allow it to expand and contract

For these reasons, it is very important that wood be properly dried before being used for cabinetwork. Commercially available lumber is either air-dried or kiln-dried. Lumber may be air-dried down to about 20% moisture content in most climates. However, lower moisture-content levels are possible only under favorable climate and temperature conditions. The use of drying kilns allows very accurate control of moisture and allows the wood to be dried down to the desired 6% to 8% moisture-content level.

Obviously, kiln-dried lumber should be specified for all cabinetwork.

CABINETMAKING WOODS

Hundreds of woods are used commercially for lumber and veneers for various purposes. Many of these can and have been used for cabinetmaking. However, there are relatively few woods that are used in large quantities for cabinet-making. Red oak and birch are two of the traditionally popular woods for residential cabinets. White oak, Philippine mahogany, cherry, white ash, alder, black walnut, maple, and pecan are all used to some extent; so are some softwoods, such as Douglas fir and several of the pines.

Characteristics of some of the most popular cabinet woods are described below.

Birch (Figure 4-11).   A dense, fairly heavy hardwood, birch has a number of characteristics that make it one of the most popular of cabinet woods. It machines well and accepts stains and finishes well. It has very small pores and, when finished, has a uniform hard surface that is easy to clean. The heartwood is a light reddish brown, and the sapwood is a yellowish white. Birch is also readily available in plywood in select white (all sapwood), select red (all heartwood), or unselect (a mixture of heartwood and sapwood).

Red oak (Figure 4-12).   This wood is very hard, fairly heavy, and strong. It is ring-porous, and the pores are quite large and easily visible without magnification, as are medullary rays. The heartwood is a light red to pink in color, and the sapwood is a yellowish white. The grain pattern is usually quite prominent. Oak cabinets are very durable and attractive.

White oak (Figure 4-13).   White oak is somewhat similar to red oak in appearance, although its color tends to be a yellowish brown. It also has large pores, but they are not quite as visible since they are filled with a material called tyloses. White oak is usually somewhat more expensive than red oak. It is also very hard and durable.

Figure 4-11 Birch

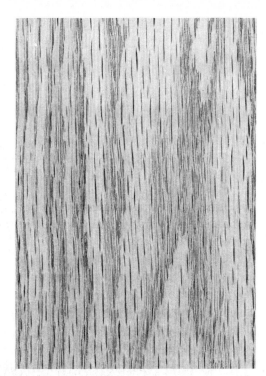

Figure 4-12 Red oak

Figure 4-13 White oak

Philippine mahogany (Figure 4-14). A number of wood species are sold as Philippine mahogany. They are all relatively soft, very open-grained woods. They range in color from a very light pinkish white to a deep reddish brown. They are relatively inexpensive, and they machine easily. They accept stain readily, but because of their porous nature they usually require a paste wood filler if a smooth finish is to be obtained.

Hard maple (Figure 4-15). A very dense, very hard wood, hard maple is diffuse-porous, with a very fine texture and grain. The heartwood is very light brown and the sapwood nearly white. It is somewhat difficult to machine as it tends to chip or tear out if machined against the grain. Because of its fine, dense grain and its hardness, it is an excellent wood for cutting boards.

Black walnut (Figure 4-16). This is the aristocrat of the American cabinet and furniture woods and is one of the most expensive. It has a very rich, dark brown heartwood with a light yellowish brown sapwood. It is an excellent machining wood with a fine, fairly uniform texture.

Alder (Figure 4-17). Until fairly recently, alder was used primarily as a firewood. However, it has found wide commercial acceptance in recent years and is often used in cabinetmaking. It is a light, fairly uniform brown wood, somewhat similar in appearance to the heartwood of birch, although it is much softer. It is quite often used for face frames on birch cabinets. It has a uniform texture and machines easily. It accepts stain well and is often used to imitate more costly woods.

Cherry (Figure 4-18). Cherry is an excellent furniture wood that is sometimes used for cabinetmaking. It is quite expensive but has very attractive coloring and grain patterns. The heartwood is predominantly a reddish brown, but traces of other colors such as green sometimes appear. The sapwood is a yellowish white. It is a nice machining wood, although it does tend to get burn marks if the wood is not moved past the cutters at a uniform speed or if the cutters are dull.

White ash (Figure 4-19). A very hard, strong wood, white ash has the capability to withstand shock loads well, which makes it popular for baseball bats and handles for axes and hammers. It is occasionally used in cabinetmaking. It is a very open-grained wood that is a very light yellow brown in color. It has a slight resemblance to certain oaks but does not have oak's highly visible medullary rays.

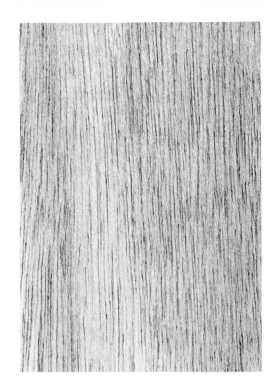

Figure 4-14 Philippine mahogany

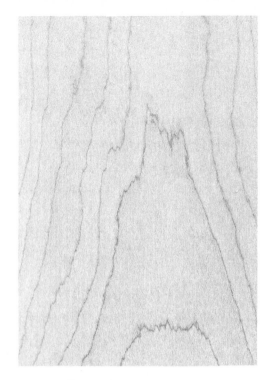

Figure 4-15 Hard maple

Figure 4-16 Black walnut

Figure 4-17 Alder

Figure 4-18 Cherry

Figure 4-19 White ash

METHODS OF CUTTING LUMBER

The way in which a log is sawn into boards determines the appearance of the boards and also determines the shrinkage and strength characteristics of the boards. Figure 4-20 shows the most common method, known as plain sawing. Plain sawing is the least expensive method and results in the least waste. Figure 4-21 shows the quarter-sawn method, in which the log is quartered and then

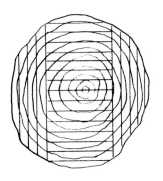

Figure 4-20 Plain-sawn lumber

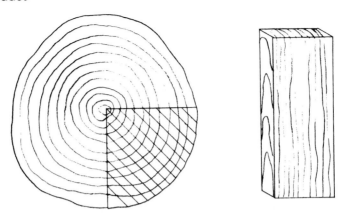

Figure 4-21 Quarter-sawn lumber

the boards are cut perpendicular to the growth rings. This method is considerably more expensive than the plain-sawn method and results in more waste material. However, the boards are less likely to shrink in width and tend to be more stable.

LUMBER GRADES

Lumber is a natural product, and no two boards are exactly alike. Many boards have characteristics that limit their usefulness for certain applications. A board may have a large knot, causing a weak spot that would render the board useless for structural applications. Another board may have a fungus stain that detracts from its appearance but would have no effect on its strength. Because of these and other problems, it has been necessary to develop a fairly complex system of grading boards based on their expected use so that the purchaser is assured of getting a product that will do the intended job. Traditionally, most softwood lumber has been used in fairly large boards for structural applications such as framing buildings, while hardwoods have been cut into smaller pieces for remanufacture into furniture and cabinets. Therefore, many of the softwood grades are based on the assumption that the entire board is to be used in one piece, and a large knot would downgrade the entire piece. Hardwoods, on the other hand, are usually graded on the percentage of usable wood (or clear cuttings) in a board, so a large knot would not necessarily be a serious defect in an otherwise clear board.

The actual grading specifications, in most cases, are developed by associations of lumber manufacturers. There are many grading classifications for various species of wood, and some of them are quite complex. It is not necessary for the cabinetmaker to have a thorough understanding of all the grading rules to make an intelligent selection of lumber. Of the multitude of grades and types of lumber available, only a few are intended for remanufacture into cabinets and millwork. A brief description of some of these grades follows.

Softwood grades.   Softwood lumber is generally classified according to *use, degree of manufacture*, and *size* for grading purposes.

Under the *use* classification, there are three categories: *yard lumber*, which includes light framing lumber; *structural lumber*, which is stress-rated for heavy framing; and *factory or shop lumber*, which is intended for remanufacture. This factory or shop category is of most interest to the cabinetmaker, since this lumber is intended to be remanufactured into such articles as sash and doors, cabinets, and other millwork. Shop lumber is usually sold S2S (surfaced two sides) in the following thicknesses:

- 4/4 S2S to 25/32 in.
- 5/4 S2S to 1 5/32 in.
- 6/4 S2S to 1 13/32 in.
- 8/4 S2S to 1 13/16 in.

Unlike softwood lumber intended for building construction, shop-grade lumber is graded on the basis of the number of usable cuttings that can be obtained from a board. The top grade of 4/4 (1 in.) shop lumber is called *factory select* (No. 3 clear) and must yield 70% or more clear cuttings of specified sizes. (Some typical sizes are 9 1/2 in. wide by 18 in. long and 5 in. wide by 3 ft. long.) *No. 1 shop* is the next grade and must yield between 50% and 70% clear cuttings (allowing some smaller cuttings). *No. 2 shop* must yield not less than 33 1/3% clear cuttings.

Hardwood grades.   The cabinetmaker is probably more concerned with hardwood grades than with softwoods. Fortunately, the grading system is less confusing. The grades that are most readily available are firsts and seconds (combined as one grade and abbreviated FAS), No. 1 common, and No. 2 common. Although the actual specifications for each grade are quite complex, one may assume that the FAS grade is approximately 90% usable, No. 1 common approximately 66.7% usable, and No. 2 common approximately 50% usable. There are also several other grades, but they are seldom sold.

LUMBER SIZES

Lumber is available rough-sawn, S2S (surfaced two sides) or S4S (surfaced four sides). Hardwood lumber is quite often purchased rough-sawn in 1- or

Table 4-1 NOMINAL AND FINISHED SIZES OF PLANED LUMBER

Thickness		Width	
Nominal	Planed	Nominal	Planed
1 in.	3/4 in.	2 in.	1 1/2 in.
2 in.	1 1/2 in.	4 in.	3 1/2 in.
		6 in.	5 1/2 in.
		8 in.	7 1/4 in.
		10 in.	9 1/4 in.
		12 in.	11 1/4 in.

2-in. thicknesses and random widths. It is also usually available in S2S form, in which case 1-in. lumber is surfaced to either 13/16 in. or 25/32 in. This lumber is intended for eventual use at 3/4-in. thickness for face frames or door frames. While 1 in. and 2 in. are the most common thicknesses, others are available. These are sometimes listed by quarters: 4/4 in., 5/4 in., 8/4 in., and so on. Five-quarter lumber surfaced to 1 1/16 in. is often used for stair treads, for example. Softwood lumber in the factory or shop grade is also often surfaced 25/32 in. for remanufacture into cabinet and furniture parts or moldings. However, most softwood lumber is surfaced four sides to standard thicknesses and widths. Table 4-1 shows the nominal and finished dimensions of dry-planed softwood lumber.

DETERMINING LUMBER QUANTITIES

Planed softwood lumber sold through retail outlets is usually sold by the linear foot. Most other lumber is sold by the board foot, quite often in 1,000 bd. ft. units. The board foot is a volume measurement: 1 bd. ft. is equal to 144 cu. in. of wood. The so-called standard board foot is 1 in. thick, 12 in. wide, and 12 in. long (144 cu. in.). Any combination of thickness, width, and length resulting in 144 cu. in. is 1 bd. ft. A board 2 in. by 6 in. by 12 in., a board 1 in. by 1 in. by 144 in., and a board 1 in. by 6 in. by 24 in. each contains 1 bd. ft. To calculate the number of board feet in a given board, the three dimensions of the board, expressed in inches, must be multiplied to give the number of cubic inches. To convert this to board feet, merely divide by 144. Thus, the formula is

$$\frac{T \text{ in.} \times W \text{ in.} \times L \text{ in.}}{144} = \text{Bd. ft.}$$

where T = thickness in inches, W = width in inches, and L = length in inches. If the length is expressed in feet, the total is divided by 12 as follows:

$$\frac{\text{T in.} \times \text{W in.} \times \text{L ft.}}{12} = \text{Bd. ft.}$$

When estimating the number of board feet of lumber in a cabinet for the purpose of purchasing material, applying the formula to the various parts of the cabinet will only give the number of board feet in the finished product. This does not make allowance for cutting and planing parts to size. The amount of extra material required will vary greatly, depending on how efficiently the sizes can be cut from the rough boards. The actual extra amount that must be purchased will probably be at least 25% and may be much higher.

SHEET MATERIALS

Plywood.   Plywood is a sheet material designed to take advantage of the fact that wood is very strong in the direction of the grain and that it shrinks very little in that direction. It is made by gluing alternate layers of wood at right angles to one another. Consequently, the strength properties tend to be more nearly equal across the width and length of the sheet. It also tends to be more stable than solid boards.

This construction gives plywood a number of other properties that make it especially useful as a cabinetmaking material. Unlike solid lumber, it has no tendency to check and split near the ends, even when nails are driven near the end. It is available with a number of attractive wood veneers on the surface. One of its biggest advantages as a cabinet material is that it is available presanded in large sheets and is ready to be cut to finished sizes. This saves many hours of work when compared with gluing solid boards together to make cabinet parts. Hardwood plywood is usually used for finished ends, finished backs, and sometimes for cabinet doors, drawer fronts, and shelves. Softwood plywood is usually used for cabinet backs and sometimes for drawer bottoms.

Softwood plywoods are usually available in 1/4-in., 3/8-in., 5/8-in., 3/4-in., and 1 1/8-in. thicknesses in sheets 4 ft. by 8 ft.

Hardwood plywoods are available in 1/4-in., 3/8-in., 1/2-in., and 3/4-in. thicknesses, with the 1/4-in. and 3/4-in. sizes the most readily available.

The veneers that make up softwood plywood sheets are graded for appearance using the letters A, B, C, D, and N according to standards developed by the American Plywood Association. N is a special grade for natural finish with no defects. In practice, it is rarely available. A is the next-best grade and allows a certain number of neatly made repairs. D is the lowest grade, permitting a number of open knots and other defects. A sheet labeled A-D would have a good surface on the A face and a number of exposed defects on the D face and thus would be suitable for exposure only on one side. Softwood plywoods are also classified as being interior type or exterior type. The two major factors determining whether a sheet is rated interior or exterior are the types of adhesives used (exterior type requires a waterproof adhesive) and the quality of veneer used. An exterior sheet of plywood cannot have a D-grade veneer on the surface or in the core. Much interior-type plywood is manufactured with waterproof adhesives, but because D-grade veneers are used, it cannot be sold as exterior plywood and will not meet building code requirements for exterior applications.

Hardwood plywoods use a numbered grading system for grading the veneers except for the premium grade (A). The grades and their general requirements are listed here:

- *Premium grade (A):* Only very minor defects permitted. Any edge joints must be tight and must be matched for grain and color.
- *Good grade (1):* Edge joints must be tight, but color and grain matching is not required. Sharp color or grain contrasts are not permitted.
- *Second grade (2):* Veneer must be free of open defects. Grain and color matching is not required.
- *Utility grade (3):* Open defects are permitted.
- *Backing grade (4):* Similar to grade 3 but allows larger and more open defects.

Plywoods graded A-2 are often used for cabinet finished ends, while A-3 is often used for backs and drawer bottoms where only one side is exposed. Hardwood plywoods are also type-graded, based on their ability to withstand moisture exposure. Type I is waterproof; types II and III have progressively less resistance to moisture.

The core in hardwood plywoods may be constructed in one of three basic methods. These include veneer core, lumber core, and particle-board (or medium-density fiberboard) core. These are shown in Figure 4-22.

Veneers for both hardwood and softwood plywoods may be cut from logs by a number of methods, three of which are shown in Figure 4-23. The method used determines the appearance of the veneer and affects the cost of the plywood sheet. Rotary-cut veneer is usually the least expensive. This process involves mounting the log in a large lathe and rotating the log while a long knife blade is used to peel a continuous layer of veneer from the log, much like unrolling a roll of paper towels. The veneer comes off in a continuous roll and is then cut to desired widths.

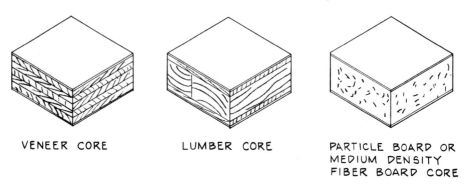

VENEER CORE   LUMBER CORE   PARTICLE BOARD OR
                                                     MEDIUM DENSITY
                                                     FIBER BOARD CORE

Figure 4-22 Plywood construction

Flat or plain slicing is somewhat more expensive and involves slicing successive layers of veneer from the log. Adjacent layers of veneer are then edge-matched when used on the face of premium-grade panels. Quarterslicing is the third, and most expensive, of the popular veneer-cutting methods. It involves cutting the log into quarters and then slicing the veneer layers perpendicular to the growth rings. These layers again are kept in sequence and matched across the face of the plywood panel.

Several other veneer-cutting methods are sometimes used to take advantage of the characteristics of certain woods, but such veneers are usually only available on special order.

Veneers may be matched using a book match, in which successive veneers are opened up as a book would be opened, or they may be slip-matched, in which case the figure is repeated with each sheet (Figure 4-24).

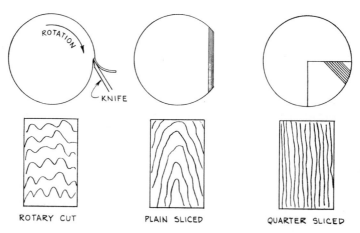

ROTARY CUT   PLAIN SLICED   QUARTER SLICED

Figure 4-23 Three common veneer-cutting methods and resulting grain patterns

BOOK MATCH

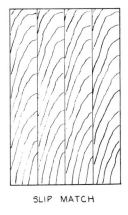

SLIP MATCH

Figure 4-24 Two common methods of veneer-matching for plywood

These two methods are usually used for veneer matching on plywood sheets. Occasionally, however, the cabinetmaker may wish to obtain a special effect using veneer matches not available in plywood. Matched sets of veneers called flitches are available; the cabinetmaker can glue these to another surface (usually particle board or plywood) to achieve the desired effect. Two popular veneer-matching methods, known as the diamond match and the reverse diamond match, are shown in Figure 4-25.

In practice, veneer matching involves cutting the veneers with straight edges and then edge-gluing the veneers together. These pieces are held together with tape until they are glued to the substrate with a wood glue and a veneer press. If a veneer press is not available, contact cement may be used. Needless to say, this is a very exacting process and requires considerable practice.

Particle board. Particle board is a manufactured sheet product made from wood chips bonded together with an adhesive. It is an engineered

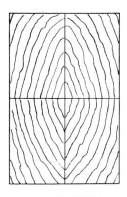

DIAMOND MATCH

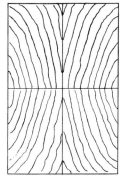

REVERSE DIAMOND

Figure 4-25 Two common veneer-matching methods

product, designed for a number of different applications. The two most readily available types are the underlayment type and the industrial type. The underlayment type is designed for use for floors under carpet or resilient floor coverings and should not be used for cabinetwork. The industrial type has a smaller chip size, which makes it easier to machine and finish, and it has a higher density (usually about 45 to 50 lb./cu. ft.). It is generally available in 1/2-in. and 3/4-in. thicknesses in 49-in. by 97-in. sheet size.

Particle board is an excellent material for many cabinet applications. It is very stable, with little tendency to warp since it has no grain direction. It machines easily and is easy to glue and assemble with conventional and pneumatic fasteners. It is also available with a filled and sanded surface, ready to finish. It is used a great deal for nonexposed cabinet parts such as bottoms, partitions, shelves, wall ends, and countertops.

Hardboard.   Hardboard is another sheet product, but instead of being made from wood chips like particle board, the wood is broken down to fibers and then consolidated under heat and pressure in a hot press. The resulting board ranges from tan to dark brown in color and has a very dense, smooth surface. It is water-resistant and can be easily cut, machined, and finished.

Hardboard is available in 4-ft. by 8-ft. sheets, in thicknesses ranging from 1/8 in. to 3/8 in., with some special applications available up to 1 in. in thickness. The most common thicknesses are 1/8 in., 3/16 in., and 1/4 in.

Hardboard is available in standard and tempered types. The standard type is sold as it comes from the press and has all the properties previously described. Tempered hardboard has improved hardness and abrasion resistance and is made by subjecting standard hardboard to a treatment of heat, oil, and chemicals. Hardboard is available smooth on one side with a screen-finish back, smooth on both sides, or in a number of embossed or punched patterns. Its primary applications in cabinetwork are cabinet backs, vertical dividers, and drawer bottoms, and some of the embossed or punched patterns are used as door panels.

Hardboards for cabinet backs are available prepainted to match some of the laminated particle boards used on frameless cabinet construction.

Medium-density fiberboard.   Medium-density fiberboard is a relatively new product for cabinetmaking. It is similar to particle board in appearance and applications, but it is made from wood fibers in the manner of hardboard. This construction results in a smoother surface finish than particle board, especially on exposed edges. It enjoys great popularity in the furniture industry because its smooth surface allows a wood-grain appearance to be printed on the surface using offset presses, just as a color photograph is printed on paper for a book. It has excellent machining qualities and is often used in core stock for plywood.

Although it is somewhat more expensive than particle board, medium-density fiberboard can be used anywhere that particle board is used in cabinets. It is especially popular for drawer sides for low-priced cabinets and is available in standard drawer-side widths with premachined grooves for the drawer bottom and a wood grain printed on the surface.

Laminated particle boards and cabinet liners.   These materials make up the bulk of the material used for frameless cabinet boxes, and some are also used for doors and drawer fronts. They are often also used for the box or case construction for traditional face-frame cabinets. Most of them use industrial-grade particle board for the core, although some are available in medium-density fiberboard. The facing may be a polyester film, a vinyl film, a melamine film, or a plastic applied in liquid form and then cured.

When used as cabinet liners, the facing material is often white or an off-white such as almond or champagne. However, facing materials are available in an almost unlimited range of solid colors and wood-grain prints. Some of them are available in a choice of textures from shiny to dull as well. Many of them are available in 1/4-in. thickness for cabinet backs and either 5/8-in. or 3/4-in. thickness for cabinet boxes.

The choice of which board to use may depend on the color or pattern available, the availability of matching edge banding, and the necessary physical properties such as wear, impact, heat, and chemical resistance. Some of the materials are more resistant than others to chipping when cutting. This can be important if they must be cut on a table saw with no scoring blade.

Polyester-laminated particle boards are preferred by many shops for their resistance to chipping and for their wear and heat resistance. They are also resistant to many chemicals, including lacquer thinner, as well as being very resistant to the normal scuffing that occurs from shop handling of materials. The board is made by applying a special polyester-saturated laminating paper to one or both sides of a particle-board sheet. The lamination and curing of the sheet occurs at the same time that heat and pressure are applied. The laminated sheet is permanently fused to the particle-board substrate. The polyester resin is a thermosetting resin that provides excellent heat resistance when cured. Polyester laminates are usually somewhat more expensive than vinyl or melamine. They are used for cabinet-box components and sometimes for doors and drawer fronts. However, if heavy-duty use is anticipated, it is probably better to use high-pressure plastic laminate for doors and drawer fronts.

Melamine low-pressure laminates are used for many of the same applications and have many similar characteristics. Melamine laminates are also made in much the same way except that melamine resins rather than polyester resins are used to saturate the laminating paper. Melamine resin is also thermosetting and results in a product with good heat resistance. However, they do have slightly lower wear, impact, and stain resistance. They are generally somewhat lower in cost.

The American Laminators Association has established performance standards for thermoset (polyester and melamine) laminated panels. The American Laminators Association is a nonprofit trade association whose members produce decorative, thermally fused panels. Panels certified by the ALA must meet quite stringent performance standards. The performance standard is presented in Figure 4-26.

Tests for Resistance to:	Test Description[3]	Minimum Requirements to Comply with ALA 1988		NEMA LD3-1985 GP-20 Minimum Performance Standard
		Solid Colors	Wood Grains	
Wear	A measure of the ability of a decorative overlaid surface to maintain its design or color when subjected to prolonged abrasive wear.	400 cycles	125 cycles	200 cycles
Scuff	A measure of the ability of a decorative overlaid surface to maintain its original appearance when subjected to prolonged scraping or scuffing.	No effect	No effect	No effect
Stain	A measure of the ability of a decorative overlaid surface to resist any discoloration or marring by prolonged contact from 29 common household agents.	No effect 1-23. Moderate 24-29.	No effect 1-23. Moderate 24-29.	No effect 1-23. Moderate 24-29.
Cleanability	A measure of the ability of a decorative overlaid surface to be cleaned following prolonged contact with 15 soiling agents, using a sponge scrubbing device.	No effect. Surface cleaned in 25 or fewer strokes.	No effect. Surface cleaned in 25 or fewer strokes.	25 cycles max.
Light	A measure of the ability of a decorative overlaid surface to retain its color after prolonged exposure to a light source having a frequency range approximating sunlight.	Slight	Slight	Slight
High Temperature	A measure of the ability of a decorative overlaid surface to maintain its color and surface texture when a hot pot of 180°C (356°F) is placed on it for 20 minutes.	Slight	Slight	Slight
Radiant Heat	A measure of the ability of a decorative overlaid surface to resist any damage when subjected to a radiant-heat source under controlled laboratory conditions.	No effect after 60 seconds.	No effect after 60 seconds.	No effect after 60 seconds.
Boiling Water[4]	A measure of the ability of a decorative overlaid surface to maintain its color and surface texture when subjected to boiling water for a period of 20 minutes.	No effect	No effect	No effect
Impact	A measure of the ability of a decorative overlaid surface to resist fracture due to the impact of a 1/2-pound steel ball dropped from a measured height.	15" without fracture	15" without fracture	15" without fracture

(1) American Laminators Association (ALA) is a non-profit trade association whose member manufacturers produce decorative thermoset panels by hot press laminating polyester or melamine resin impregnated, self-bonding (minimum of 50% resin content) paper to any cellulosic substrate. It is the sponsor of the proprietary standard set forth in this document and known as the Performance Standard for Thermoset Decorative Panels, ALA 1988.

(2) This standard applies to decorative panel faces only.

(3) These test procedures are identical to those used by the National Electrical Manufacturers Association (NEMA) for testing high-pressure decorative laminates. The minimum requirements to comply with ALA 1988 for SOLID COLORS meet or exceed NEMA Standard LD3-1985 for high-pressure decorative laminates.

(4) Melamine panels, when produced under conditions for optimum panel performance, may show a slight effect.

(5) If it is established that a shipment is more than five percent (5%) below the minimum requirements to comply with each of the tests of this performance standard, the shipment has failed to meet the requirements of ALA 1988.

Figure 4-26 Performance standards for laminated boards. (Courtesy of American Laminators Association)

Many manufacturers will supply results of how their products fared when subjected to these tests. This allows for comparison between brands and between polyester and melamine.

Vinyl-laminated panels are made by gluing a vinyl film to either industrial particle board or medium-density fiberboard. This vinyl film is usually between 3 and 8 mils thick. It is a thermoplastic material and has low heat resistance. Decorative vinyl films are available in a wide range of solid colors and wood grains. They may be printed on either the face side or the back side of the film. Back-side printing gives better pattern wear resistance. Vinyls in general show good abrasion resistance and good impact resistance. They have low resistance to some solvents and low heat resistance, as well as a tendency to show burnish marks if rubbed by a hard object. They require greater care in shop handling than polyester-laminated panels do. Vinyl panels are less expensive than polyester or melamine.

There are also particle-board panels in which the decorative surface is applied in liquid form and then cured on the surface. Willamette Industries' KorTron is such a product. The panels are coated with an acrylic liquid that is cured by a process known as electron beam curing. This produces an extremely hard, smooth surface with excellent wear resistance. The panels are available in a variety of colors and wood-grain prints and are recommended for vertical and low-wear horizontal surfaces. The finishes can be supplied on one side or both sides of sheets that are from 1/4 in. to 1 in. thick.

HIGH-PRESSURE PLASTIC LAMINATES

Plastic laminates are widely used for countertop coverings and for exterior surfaces on frameless cabinets. They are very hard, durable sheets that resist heat and stains and are easy to clean. They are popularly known by brand names such as Formica and Nevamar. Particle board that has been pre-laminated can also be purchased from many manufacturers. These laminates are made by impregnating kraft paper with phenolic resins and then laminating these layers in a hot press at very high pressure. Also included in the lamination are a pattern sheet, which may have a printed wood grain or other pattern, and a transparent cover sheet.

The sheets that are intended for general-purpose use are 1/16 in. thick. Sheets intended for vertical applications such as cabinet faces are 1/32 in. thick. They are usually applied to particle board or plywood using contact cement and are applied after the cabinet is constructed. However, many large production shops laminate sheets of plastic laminate to the particle board or plywood core stock in large presses before cutting component parts.

Plastic laminates should always be applied to both surfaces of any part subject to warping. Inexpensive balance sheets are available for surfaces that won't show.

EDGE BANDING

The advent of the frameless cabinet construction system has made edge banding a much more important part of cabinetmaking. Edge banding can consist of solid wood strips, thin wood veneers, plastic-laminate strips, continuous plastic edge-banding materials, and plastic t-banding.

Solid wood strips are used to edge-band plywood and may be used for decorative effect with laminated particle boards. They may be applied by gluing and clamping, or nailing, with wafer plate joints, or with some of the larger edge-banding machines. Thin wood edge banding may also be applied with contact cement.

Wood veneer edge banding is available preglued with a heat-sensitive adhesive for iron-on application or for application with one of the heated-platen edge banders. It is also available without pregluing for application with an automatic edge bander. They are made in long coils by finger-jointing lengths of veneer together. Careful color and grain matching makes these finger joints nearly invisible.

This veneer edge banding is available with a thin fleece backing. The backing reinforces the finger joints, gives the veneer greater stability, and helps eliminate splintering, chipping, and cracking. Wood veneer edge banding is available sanded or unsanded and in several thicknesses. Thicker veneers have greater impact resistance but thin veneers are needed to laminate profile shapes or around sharp curves.

One of the major edge-banding manufacturers, Woodtape, offers preglued veneers in the following species:

Red oak	White oak
Maple	Walnut
White birch	Red birch
Ash	Cherry
African mahogany	Philippine mahogany
Honduran mahogany	Carolina pine
Western pine	Fir
Hickory	Pecan
Western cedar	Aromatic cedar
Koa	Beech

Wood tape also offers uncoated bandings for automatic edge banding in the following species:

Red oak	White oak
Walnut	Maple
Red birch	White birch
Ash	Cherry
African mahogany	Philippine mahogany
Honduran mahogany	Anigre
Teak	Elm
Carolina pine	Western pine
Ramin	Fir
Pecan	Hickory
Makore	Koto
Western cedar	Aromatic cedar
Koa	Beech

Plastic edge-banding materials are the most widely used in frameless cabinetmaking. There are three general types in popular use. These are PVC, polyester, and melamine. They are all available in a range of solid colors and wood-grain prints. They are available for automatic application or preglued, with certain exceptions to be noted later.

PVC (polyvinyl chloride) is the most popular and the least expensive. It is an extruded thermoplastic material, available in colors and textures to match most of the popular laminated particle-board panels and many high-pressure plastic laminates. The following cross-reference chart (Figure 4-27) shows how the PVC edge-banding materials of one manufacturer match the high-pressure laminates of several popular manufacturers.

Some manufacturers produce thicker PVC edge bandings that can be used in contrasting colors to provide special accent to doors, drawer fronts, or cabinet edges. They also provide extra impact resistance, and they can be routed or shaped. They are usually 3 to 5 mm thick.

Since PVC is a thermoplastic product, it has low heat resistance and does not lend itself to application with the heated-platen benchtop edge banders. Some manufacturers do supply PVC edge banding preglued for hot-air application. Glue does not bond well to PVC, so the manufacturers have to etch one side of it. PVC also has high static attraction, so dust and clippings build up on edge-bander components.

Polyester edge bandings are made by saturating special laminating papers with polyester resin and laminating them to a backing paper. They are considerably more expensive than PVC, but they are capable of withstanding the heat of the tabletop heated-platen edge banders. They are also used with automatic edge banders.

Melamine edge bandings are similar to polyester except for the use of melamine resins. Melamine and polyester edge bandings are both known for

STOCK PVC PROGRAM		FORMICA®		WILSONART®		ARBORITE®		NEVAMAR®		MICARTA®		PIONITE®	
2001	FROSTY WHITE	949	White	1573	White	S417	Snow White	S-7-4	Solid White	92M90	Cool White	SW811	White
2006	WHITE	933	Mission White					S-7-2	Chalk White			SW806	Carnation White
2115	ANTIQUE WHITE	932	Antique White	1572	Antique White	S463	Antique White	S-7-5	Antique White	90M74	Colonial White	SW803	Eggshell
2038	WHITE			1570	White	S402	White						
2008	ICE WHITE	953	Ice White	354	Designer White					92M98	Winter White	SW813	Ice White
2007	NEUTRAL WHITE	918	Neutral White					S-7-27	Smoky White	90M92	Dover White		
2114	ALMOND	920	Almond	D-30	Almond	S445	Almond	S-2-37	Almond	91M94	Almond	ST655	Almonde
2130	NATURAL ALMOND												
2209	BEIGE			1530	Beige			S-2-19	Beige	90M70	Aztec Tan	ST617	Beige
2116	LIGHT BEIGE			1531	Light Beige			S-7-25	Veutra			SW812	Tawny White
2133	DESERT BEIGE	899	Desert Beige	331	Sand	S486	Beige			52M23	Desert Beige	ST612	Pongee
2121	CHAMPAGNE	925	Champagne			S461	Eggshell	S-2-3	Champagne			ST613	Tapioca
2132	VANILLA	898	Vanilla									SY915	Vanilla
2221	PUTTY	931	Putty			S477	Doeskin	S-6-5	Putty	91M62	Silver Sand	SG209	Putty Grey
2466	W. PUTTY			1503	Putty								
2416	BLACK	909	Black	1595	Black	S405	Black	S-6-1	Black	92M16	Black	SE101	Black
2422	GREY			1500N	Grey	S488	New Silver	S-6-3	Dove Grey	90M52	Grey		
2454	FOLKSTONE	927	Folkstone	D-315	Platinum								
				D-381	Fashion Grey								
2425	FOG GREY	961	Fog			S406	Silver Grey	S-6-12	Neutral Grey	52M1110	Mercury	SG213	Opti Grey
2426	DOVE GREY			D-92	Dove Grey					92M94	Quick Silver		
2148	HAZE	921	Birch	D-97	Haze	S436	Sand						
2145	SURF	923	Surf										
2201	TIDAL SAND	917	Tidal Sand	D-46	Desert Sand			S-6-7	Oatmeal			ST606	Taupe
2240	KHAKI BROWN			D-50	Khaki Brown	S493	Toast	S-2-45	Greige	91M73	Sandy Grey		
2314	CHOCOLATE BROWN			D-34	Sienna	S490	Nugget Brown	S-2-18	Brown	90M21	Chocolate Brown	ST637	Chocolate
2301	ANGOLA BROWN	947	Angola Brown									ST604	Nubian Brown
9027	BURGUNDY	966	Burgundy							92M96	Burgundy	SR521	Burgundy
9043	MANDARIN RED			1511	Mandarin Red	S498	Fire Red	S-1-27	Liberty Red	91M33	Poppy Red		
9010	ROSE DUST			D-13	Rose-Dust	S428	Rosette			91M77	Heather Rose	SR512	Dusty Rose
9028	ROSE ASH	859	Rose Ash							91M78	Conch Shell	SR509	Rose Ash
9014	MAUVE BLUSH			D-76	Mauve Blush								
9007	MAUVE MIST			D-11	Mauve Mist							SR521	Burgundy
9044	WILD ROSE			D-98	Wild Rose								
9213	NAVY BLUE	969	Navy Blue			S440	Navy			91M25	Dark Blue	SB007	Navy Blue
1501H	WHITE HIGH GLOSS	949	White Lacquer	1573	White Gloss	S417	Snow White Gl.	S-5-7-5	Solid White Gloss	92M90	Cool White Gloss	SW811	White Gloss
1614H	ALMOND HIGH GLOSS	920	Almond Lacquer	D-30	Almond Gloss	S445	Almond Gloss	S-2-37	Almond Gloss	91M94	Almond Gloss	ST655	Almonde Gloss
1954H	FOLKSTONE HIGH GLOSS	927	Folkstone Lacquer	D-315	Platinum Gloss								
1916H	BLACK HIGH GLOSS	909	Black - Lacquer	1595	Black Gloss	S405	Black Gloss	S-6-1	Black Gloss	92M16	Black Gloss	SE101	Black Gloss
1427N	PAINTABLE												
5139	GUNSTOCK WALNUT	492	Gunstock Walnut			W340	Satellite Walnut	W-2-461 / W-8-186	Executive Walnut / Gunstock Walnut	93M69	Gunstock Walnut	WW971	Gunstock Walnut
5232	REGENCY WALNUT	385 / 232	Regency Walnut / Windsor Walnut	313	Gunstock Walnut	W245 / W105	Ambassador W. / American Walnut	W-2-686	Hallmark Walnut			WW041	Prima Walnut
5051	MONTANA WALNUT			7110	Montana Walnut	W194	Select Walnut			76M80	Designer Walnut		
5470	ENGLISH OAK			7885	English Oak	W119	English Oak			78M97	Carolina Oak	W0641	Oiled Oak
5469	F. ENGLISH OAK	343	English Oak					W-2-686	English Oak	72M08	Congress Oak		
3299	GOLDEN OAK			7888	Golden Oak	W321	Beachwood			43M73	Coastal Oak	W0571	Madison Oak
3179	BANNISTER OAK			7806	Bannister Oak								
3201	GOLD OAK												
3413	NATURAL OAK	346	Natural Oak			W373	Castle Oak	W-873	Barrel Oak	74J60	Arsenal Oak		
3407	NORTHERN OAK	7152	Northern Oak	7042	Sheril Walnut	W375	Blonde Pecan	W-8-164	Rustic Oak			W0951	Fine Oak
3434	COUNTRY OAK	7149	Country Oak			W381	Renaissance Oak	W-8-183	Country Oak			WN681	Plaza Pecan
3181	GOLDEN ASH			7817	Oregon Oak			W-8-110	Golden Ash				
3298	VALLEY PECAN	7189	Douglaston Pecan	P361	Valley Pecan								
3394	HONEY TEAK	417	Honey Tone Teak	1323	Brn. Indian Teak	W100	East Indian Teak	W-2-552	Light Teakwood	96M23	Ceylon Teak	WT601	Scandia Teak
3021	DESIGNERS OAK	7185	Royal Oak										
3264	SYLVAN OAK												
3249	SLICED RED OAK			W230	Sliced Red Oak							W0891	Sherwood Oak

Figure 4-27 Cross-reference chart for matching PVC edge banding to high-pressure laminates. (Courtesy of Woodtape Inc.)

their "laminate" appearance, that is, their ability to exactly duplicate the appearance of high-pressure laminate sheets. This makes them ideal bonding materials for doors and drawer fronts where high-pressure laminates are used. They are also nonstatic.

Polyesters have limited availability in some colors such as blues and greens.

ADHESIVES

A number of woodworking adhesives on the market will, if properly used, yield a wood joint stronger than the wood itself. However, they vary in such characteristics as water resistance, heat resistance, chemical resistance, curing time, and gap-filling properties.

For general cabinetwork joinery, a high degree of water resistance is usually not necessary, although cutting boards should be assembled with a water- and heat-resistant adhesive. Traditionally, woodworking adhesives have been rated in three categories on the basis of moisture resistance: *low moisture resistance*, in which the adhesives do not have to meet any particular standard; *water-resistant*, in which certain prescribed standards must be met; and *waterproof*, a category that has very rigorous standards and requires that the wood fibers break down before the glue line fails.

Curing time is an important consideration in cabinetmaking. If it were necessary to leave each subassembly of a cabinet clamped overnight to cure, the total assembly time would be very long. Therefore, glue with a short curing time is usually desirable except in situations where a complex structure must be assembled in one operation. In such a case, an adhesive with a slow drying time should be selected to allow for getting all the component parts properly clamped and adjusted before the curing begins.

If all joints to be glued are accurately fitted so that there is a high level of contact between mating surfaces, the gap-filling properties of a glue are of little importance. If it becomes necessary to fit parts that are not perfectly mated, however, it is necessary to have an adhesive with good gap-filling properties. Some adhesives are very good at filling small gaps with little loss of strength, while others form a very brittle joint under the same conditions.

Following are descriptions of some of the more popular cabinetmaking adhesives.

Aliphatic resin glue.   This yellow, ready-to-use glue has a very short clamping time (30 to 45 min. at room temperature), excellent gap-filling properties, good heat resistance, and low moisture resistance. It is probably the most popular glue for assembling cabinets. But its short assembly time makes complex assembly operations difficult.

Polyvinyl resin.   This white, ready-to-use glue is another popular woodworking glue when moisture and heat resistance are not required. It has a fairly short drying time of approximately 1 hr., but a slightly longer assembly time than the aliphatic resin, an advantage in complex assembly situations. It has good gap-filling properties. It is also quite inexpensive.

Liquid hide glue.   This brown, ready-to-use glue is sometimes used when a very long assembly time is expected. It sets slowly, giving considerable time for final adjustment of component parts. Its curing time in clamps is 10 to 12 hr. It has fair gap-filling properties and low moisture resistance.

Powdered plastic resin.   This adhesive is sold in powdered form and is mixed with water just before being used. It has very high moisture and heat resistance. It forms a very strong joint when parts are accurately fitted but tends to be somewhat brittle when used with poor-fitting joints. Curing at room temperature takes 12 to 14 hr. But the resin's slow curing time and poor gap-filling properties can be disadvantages, and its strength is subject to following proper mixing procedures. The glue is good for only 2 to 3 hr. after mixing.

Contact cement.   Contact cement is not really a woodworking glue in the same category as the previously listed adhesives and is not recommended for general assembly of wood joints. It is, however, used extensively in cabinet-making for applying plastic laminate countertops and occasionally for applying thin edge-band material to plywood edges. It is a rubber-based cement which, unlike the previously mentioned adhesives, requires no clamping. Both surfaces to be joined are coated and allowed to dry. They are then brought together and a momentary pressure is applied to complete the bond. The drying process takes place by solvent evaporation, and the drying time required before assembly of the parts will vary from 10 to 20 min. at room temperature for solvent-based cements to 1 hr. or more for water-based cements.

Several other adhesives are occasionally used in cabinetmaking for specific purposes. These include casein glue, which is good for gluing oily tropical woods and is one of the few adhesives that will cure at any temperature above freezing. Another is resorcinol resin, a two-part waterproof adhesive that is mixed before using. It is very expensive and is usually used only when a totally waterproof joint is needed. Epoxies are also expensive and are used for gluing dissimilar materials, such as wood to metal, ceramics, or glass.

All the adhesives mentioned, except for the contact cement, require that the parts being glued be tightly clamped together during the curing period.

FASTENERS

Component parts may be fastened together using nails, staples, screws, bolts, and other fasteners in addition to adhesives. These may be either hand-driven or air-driven. Frameless cabinets may be assembled with special screws.

Nails.   While there are many different types of nails for various purposes, only a few types are used for most cabinet assembly. They are shown in Figure 4-28. Of the types shown, most work is assembled with box nails, finishing nails, and brads. Nail sizes are designated with an antiquated system that uses penny sizes (abbreviated d) to indicate the length of the nail. A

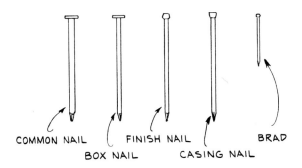

COMMON NAIL   FINISH NAIL   BRAD

BOX NAIL   CASING NAIL

Figure 4-28 Nails used for cabinet assembly

2-penny (or 2d) nail is 1 in. long. Each additional penny adds 1/4 in. to the length, so a 3d nail is 1 1/4 in. long, a 4d nail is 1 1/2 in. long, and so on to 3 in.

Screws. Wood screws are used when a stronger joint is needed than can be obtained by nailing, or when it may be necessary to dissemble a joint. They are available with a round head, flat head, oval head, or bugle head, as shown in Figure 4-29.

The round head is generally used in applications where finished appearance is not important.

Flat-head and bugle-head screws are usually countersunk beneath the surface and covered by a wood plug. Oval-head screws are used in exposed locations and are usually used with a finish washer. They are often bright-plated or finished to match other cabinet hardware.

Screw length is designated in inches and fractions of an inch. Thickness is designated by the gauge size of the shank.

The screw heads may have either a straight slot, Phillips slot, or square recess. The Phillips or square recess is preferred for cabinetwork because it makes the screws much easier to power-drive.

Pneumatic fasteners. The advent of pneumatic staplers and nailers has greatly reduced the time required for traditional cabinet assembly. Figure 4-30 shows two pneumatic nailers, and Figure 4-31 shows two staplers. Staples are usually used on surfaces that will not be exposed, since they leave a relatively large hole in the wood surface. They do have advantages over nails

FINISH WASHER

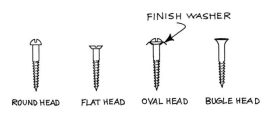

ROUND HEAD   FLAT HEAD   OVAL HEAD   BUGLE HEAD

Figure 4-29 Wood screws used for cabinet assembly

Figure 4-30 Pneumatic nailers. (Courtesy of Senco Products, Inc.)

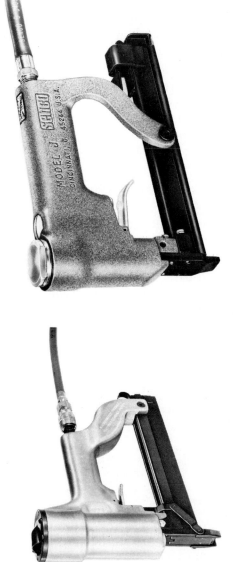

Figure 4-31 Pneumatic staplers. (Courtesy of Senco Products, Inc.)

77

in that they have less tendency to split the wood and the two legs of the staple are usually designed to "clinch" as they are driven into the wood, so they have better holding power than nails.

Finish nails are used on exposed surfaces such as face frames and finished ends. The nail gun drives the finish nail slightly below the surface to allow for filling.

There are also special guns that drive special fasteners designed to draw butt-jointed wood parts together. Figure 4-32 shows such a gun and its three fasteners.

There are several screws used for frameless construction. One of these is a special particle-board screw that is very similar to the bugle-head screw, but it has a deeper thread designed to resist pulling out of particle board.

There is also a very thick screw (Figure 4-33) designed especially for assembly of frameless cabinets. It has even better holding power in particle board. Cover caps that match the laminated particle boards are available to cover these screw holes.

The other screw used extensively in frameless construction is the system screw, or Euroscrew (Figure 4-34). It is designed for mounting cabinet hardware using the 5-mm system holes and is available in selected lengths between 10 and 30 mm.

There are also twin-mount screws (Figure 4-35) for mounting hinge-mounting plates back-to-back on a cabinet partition. There are similar connecting screws (Figure 4-36) for attaching adjoining cabinets using the 5-mm system holes.

Figure 4-32 Pneumatic driver for clamp nails for fastening butt joints. (Courtesy of Senco Products, Inc.)

Figure 4-33 Special assembly screw

Figure 4-34 System, or (Euro), screw. (Courtesy of Julius Blum, Inc.)

 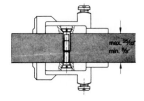

Figure 4-35 Twin-mount screw. (Courtesy of Julius Blum, Inc.)

 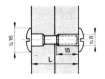

Figure 4-36 Connecting screw. (Courtesy of Julius Blum, Inc.)

CABINET HARDWARE FOR FRAMELESS CABINETS

Hinges.   The frameless cabinetmaking system was made possible by the development of special concealed hinges that mount inside the cabinet, yet allow the doors to pivot outside the cabinet. This is accomplished by recessing the hinge cup into the back side of the door. This places the actual pivot point inside the door and thus in front of the cabinet. Some of the more elaborate hinges have a series of links that allow the pivot point to move outward as the door opens so that the door can be opened as much as 170° or more without binding on an adjacent door. Frameless hinges come in two parts—the hinge, which mounts on the door, and the mounting plate, which mounts on the cabinet. The hinge arm is grooved so that it will slide over the mounting plate. It is then locked in place by tightening a screw. A typical frameless concealed hinge and mounting plate is shown in Figure 4-37.

The hinge is attached to the door by drilling a 35-mm hole for the hinge cup in the back of the door. Two screw holes will also be needed. The hinge-mounting plate is mounted inside the cabinet using two of the 5-mm system holes. See Chapter 10 for details on installing doors.

Figure 4-37 Typical hinge and mounting plate. (Courtesy of Julius Blum, Inc.)

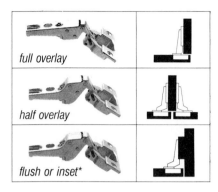

Figure 4-38 Full-overlay, half-overlay, and flush hinge. (Courtesy of Julius Blum, Inc.)

Two hinges are adequate for most typical base- and wall-cabinet doors. Larger doors or doors that have mirrors or trays mounted will require more hinges. One hinge manufacturer recommends two hinges for doors up to 15 lbs., three for 15–30 lbs., four for 30–45 lbs., and five for 45–60 lbs.

Variations of these hinges and mounting plates allow doors to be mounted in a full-overlay position, half-overlay position, or in a flush (inset) position (Figure 4-38).

The full overlay is the most common application and is used to mount doors on cabinet ends. The half-overlay application is used when the cabinet has one or more interior partitions. This allows mounting two doors on a partition or mounting a door adjacent to a bank of drawers. The flush application is used when the doors are to set inside the cabinet.

It is possible to change applications (full overlay, half overlay, or flush) by using mounting plates that are built up to different thicknesses or by using hinges with either straight or cranked arms (Figure 4-39).

For example, to obtain a full-overlay application, a hinge with a straight arm and a shallow (0 mm built-up) mounting plate could be used. To obtain a half-overlay application, the same hinge could be used with a 9-mm built-up mounting plate or by using a hinge with a cranked arm. A flush application can be obtained by using a hinge with a greater offset in the cranked arm and a shallow mounting plate or by using a 9-mm base plate and a medium cranked arm hinge or by using a straight arm hinge and a 19-mm built-up mounting plate. It is more common to change mounting plates to change applications.

Hinges are available in various degrees of door opening, from 95° to 170° or more. The lesser the degree of opening, the simpler the design of the hinge will be. The cost of the hinges goes up with the degree of opening. The greater-opening hinges are somewhat bulkier because of the extra links required to allow the pivot point to move. Figure 4-40 shows hinges that allow different degrees of opening.

There are also several special-purpose hinges. One of these is a corner-cabinet hinge that allows for mounting the door at a 45° angle in relation to

straight hinge arm

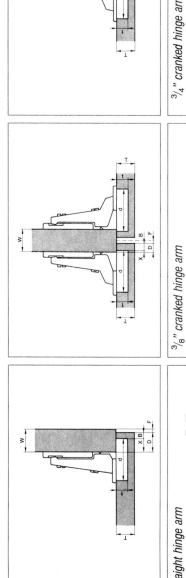

0 mm mounting plate

Corner or full overlay application, use straight hinge arm and 0 mm built up mounting plate.

³/₈" cranked hinge arm

³/₈" built up mounting plate

Half overlay or twin application, use 9,5 mm (³/₈") cranked hinge arm or straight hinge arm with 9 mm (³/₈") built-up mounting plate.

³/₄" cranked hinge arm

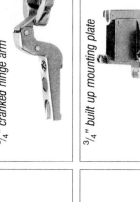

³/₄" built up mounting plate

Flush or inset application, use 18 mm (³/₄") cranked hinge arm or straight hinge arm with 19 mm (³/₄") built-up mounting plate or 9,5 mm (³/₈") cranked hinge arm with 9 mm (³/₈") built-up mounting plate.

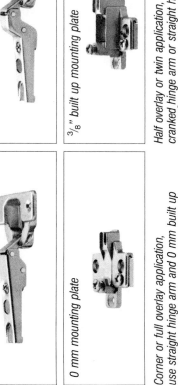

Figure 4-39 Straight and cranked arm hinges. (Courtesy of Julius Blum, Inc.)

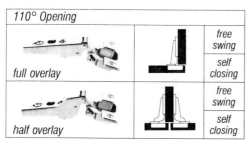

110° Opening

full overlay — free swing / self closing

half overlay — free swing / self closing

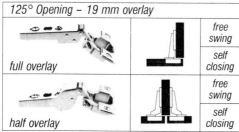

125° Opening – 19 mm overlay

full overlay — free swing / self closing

half overlay — free swing / self closing

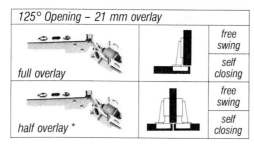

125° Opening – 21 mm overlay

full overlay — free swing / self closing

half overlay * — free swing / self closing

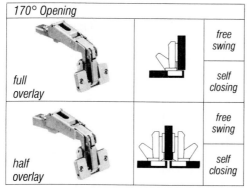

170° Opening

full overlay — free swing / self closing

half overlay — free swing / self closing

* For half overlay use 9 mm built-up mounting plate.

Figure 4-40 Hinges that allow different degrees of opening. (Courtesy of Julius Blum, Inc.)

the cabinet end (Figure 4-41). These corner cabinets are often used to house revolving Lazy Susan trays.

Another special-purpose hinge is the blind-corner-cabinet hinge designed for a situation where one cabinet extends into a room corner and another cabinet butts against it (Figure 4-42). This hinge allows mounting doors to a cabinet front panel or mounting post rather than requiring a cabinet partition.

Another special-purpose hinge is the zero-protrusion hinge, designed so that when the door is opened 90° or more from the face of the cabinet, it will be out of the way of a roll-out shelf or tray mounted directly on the cabinet side (Figure 4-43).

There are also special hinges for thick doors over 19 mm, or 3/4 in., thick.

Yet another special-purpose hinge is designed for glass doors. It is similar to the normal frameless-style hinges but is designed to mount in holes drilled

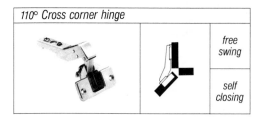

Figure 4-41 A 45°-angle cabinet hinge. (Courtesy of Julius Blum, Inc.)

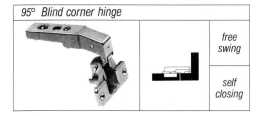

Figure 4-42 Blind-corner hinge. (Courtesy of Julius Blum, Inc.)

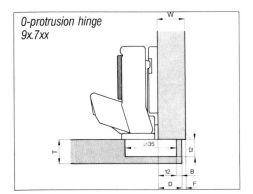

Figure 4-43 Zero-protrusion hinge. (Courtesy of Julius Blum, Inc.)

in the glass door. This hinge is available for full overlay, half overlay, and flush or inset applications.

Some companies also make versions of frameless hinges for use on face-frame cabinets. One of the major advantages of the frameless-style concealed hinges is the range of adjustment they provide. After the door is attached to the cabinet, it can be adjusted inward or outward, upward or downward, or from side to side by merely turning the adjusting screws. This makes it easy to obtain an even reveal around the doors.

Most frameless hinges are self-closing, but free-swinging versions of some models are available.

One of the newer innovations in frameless-style hinges is the clip-on hinge. The hinge is mounted on the door as usual, and the mounting plate is attached to the cabinet in the conventional manner. The door can then be mounted on the cabinet by merely pressing the back of the hinge onto the mounting plate. No tools are needed. This permits doors to be mounted and adjusted at the cabinet shop. They can then be removed for shipping and then easily remounted after the cabinets are installed. Final adjustment, if necessary, can still be made on the job.

Frameless hinges are available for either screw-on or press-on applications. In either case, the hinge cup is mounted in a 35-mm hole in the door. The screw-on versions are secured with two wood screws. The press-on hinges have the securing screws premounted in plastic dowels in the hinge cup. Two 8-mm holes are drilled adjacent to the 35-mm hole for press-on application, as shown in Figure 4-44. The hinge, with its premounted plastic dowels, is then pressed into the door. This saves time and ensures that the hinge is mounted with proper alignment. A special hinge-boring and -pressing machine, such as

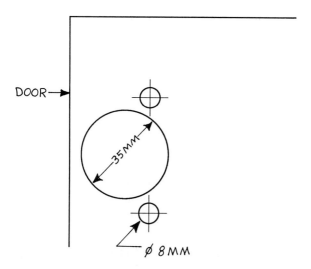

DOOR

35 MM

∅ 8 MM

Figure 4-44 Boring pattern for press-in hinges

Figure 4-45 Hinge-boring and -pressing machine. (Courtesy of Mepla Inc., Furniture Fittings)

the one shown in Figure 4-45, is necessary for using press-on hinges. These machines are available from the hinge manufacturers.

Most of the hinge manufacturers sell jigs for locating hinges on doors and hinge plates on cabinets. These are helpful if the 5-mm system holes are not used or if a hinge-boring press is not available.

Selecting frameless hinges.   Selecting a frameless hinge may be a bit confusing at first because of the many variations available. The major choices are:

- Application—full overlay, half overlay, or flush (inset)
- Degree of swing
- Self-closing or free swinging
- Press-on or screw-on application
- Mounting-plate holes sized for wood screws or Euro (system) screws

Drawer guides.   Drawer guides for frameless cabinets are not terribly dissimilar from conventional drawer guides. In fact, conventional side-mount, roller-guide drawer guides can be used with frameless cabinets.

Frameless drawer guides are designed for either side-mount or bottom-mount applications. Both types are available in standard or full-extension versions. The standard version will usually allow the drawer to open to approximately three-fourths its length, whereas the full-extension guide allows the drawer to be pulled out its full length. Full-extension guides are more expensive.

Drawer guides are available in lengths from 250 mm (10 in.) up to 600 mm (32 in.). The cabinet-mounting members usually have dual sets of mounting holes: one set of small holes to allow mounting with wood screws and the other set of large holes to allow the use of Euroscrews, or system screws. In the latter case, the 5-mm system holes in the cabinet side are used for attachment.

Side-mount drawer guides are used when the drawer side material and drawer construction do not lend themselves to installing screws in the underside of the drawer guide. A typical side-mount guide installation is shown in Figure 4-46.

Bottom-mount drawer guides actually are positioned on the drawer side, but at the very bottom edge. In fact, they extend around the bottom corner of the drawer and screw into the drawer bottom. The bottom-mount guides offer several significant advantages. The drawer guide does not have to be aligned vertically on the drawer side, but is aligned just with the bottom edge of the drawer. Bottom mount guides also support the weight of the drawer bottom so a much simpler drawer construction may be used. The drawer bottom can be butted to the drawer sides rather than set in a groove (Figure 4-47). Bottom-mount guides can also be used for roll-out trays in cabinets. Some manufacturers make guides with up, down, and sideways adjustment features.

Both the side-mount and bottom-mount guides may be used with face-frame cabinets if a special rear-mounting socket is purchased.

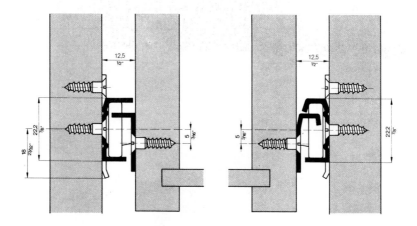

Figure 4-46 Typical side-mount drawer guide. (Courtesy of Julius Blum, Inc.)

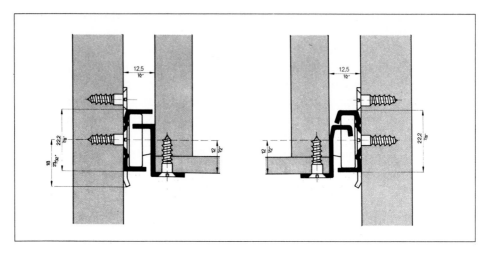

Figure 4-47 Typical bottom-mount drawer guide. (Courtesy of Julius Blum, Inc.)

Most of the drawer-guide manufacturers make mounting tools for holding drawer guides in place on the cabinet side for installation. These tools are needed only if 5-mm system holes are not used for mounting. One such tool is shown in Figure 4-48.

Several of the drawer-guide manufacturers market drawer guides that are integral with drawer sides. The cabinetmaker only supplies the drawer bottom, back, and front. This greatly reduces the time required for drawer construction. One of these systems is shown in Figure 4-49.

Most frameless-style drawer guides require 12.5 mm (1/2 in.) side clearance. Many of them have a captive-side-rail design that eliminates unnecessary side motion if that clearance is exceeded.

Door and drawer pulls.   Door and drawer pulls used in frameless cabinets are usually very simple and clean in design to complement the cabinet

Figure 4-48 Drawer-guide mounting tool for use when system holes are not used. (Courtesy of Julius Blum, Inc.)

Figure 4-49 Metal drawer side with integral guide. (Courtesy of Julius Blum, Inc.)

design. There are three types of pulls that are popular for frameless cabinets. One is the continuous pull (Figure 4-50), wood or metal recessed pulls (Figure 4-51), or wood or metal-wire pulls (Figure 4-52).

Continuous pulls are usually made of wood, although extruded aluminum ones are available. A cross section of a typical pull for a base-cabinet application and a pull for wall-cabinet applications is shown in Figure 4-53. The material is purchased in long lengths and cut to length as needed to match door and drawer widths. A groove must be machined in the top of the door or drawer front to receive the pulls (the groove will be on the bottom of a wall-cabinet door).

Figure 4-50 Wood continuous pull. (Courtesy of Julius Blum, Inc.)

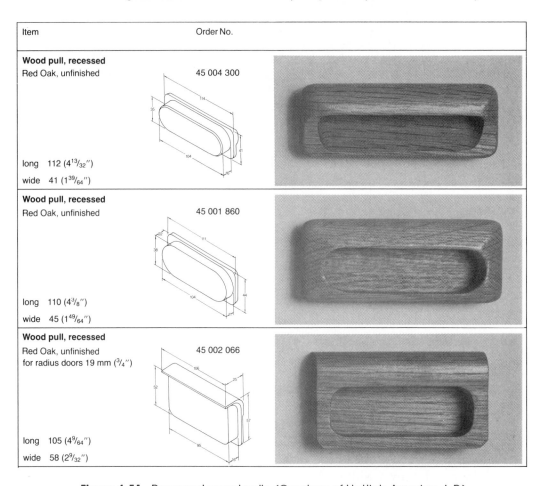

Item	Order No.	
Wood pull, recessed Red Oak, unfinished long 112 (4^{13}/$_{32}$") wide 41 (1^{39}/$_{64}$")	45 004 300	
Wood pull, recessed Red Oak, unfinished long 110 (4^{3}/$_{8}$") wide 45 (1^{49}/$_{64}$")	45 001 860	
Wood pull, recessed Red Oak, unfinished for radius doors 19 mm (^{3}/$_{4}$") long 105 (4^{9}/$_{64}$") wide 58 (2^{9}/$_{32}$")	45 002 066	

Figure 4-51 Recessed wood pulls. (Courtesy of Hettich America, L.P.)

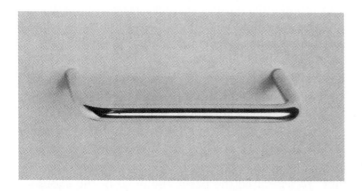

Figure 4-52 Wire pulls. (Courtesy of Hettich America, L.P.)

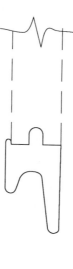

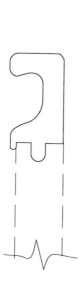

Figure 4-53 Cross section of typical continuous-pull material for base and wall cabinets

The recessed wood or metal pulls require cutting a recess in the drawer front. A jig for a router can easily be made for this purpose. Some of the pulls that appear to be recessed are actually surface mounted.

KD hardware.   KD or RTA hardware allows cabinets to be shipped disassembled and then be assembled on the job site. Frameless-style cabinets lend themselves well to this system. Each of the major frameless cabinet hardware manufacturers offers several KD or RTA systems. Many of these operate on the principle of an eccentric cam and a shoulder screw. The shoulder screw is permanently installed in one cabinet member and the eccentric cam in the other. To assemble the parts, the head of the shoulder screw is inserted into a groove in the eccentric cam. The cam is turned with a screwdriver to draw the parts together and lock them in place. A number of other systems are also used. One of these is shown in Figure 4-54.

Each system requires a specific drilling pattern in the cabinet part. The hardware manufacturer's catalog or a sales representative should be consulted.

Many of these KD systems work in conjunction with wood dowels. The dowels are used to locate the parts accurately during assembly and to provide reinforcement in the joint. The assembly fastener holds the parts tightly together.

Shelf supports.   Shelf supports for adjustable shelves are designed to be inserted in the 5-mm system holes. They are available in a variety of styles in plastic or metal. Some are designed to lock the shelf in place. Several shelf supports are shown in Figure 4-55.

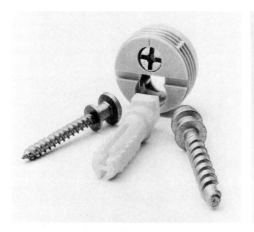 

Figure 4-54   A Typical fastening system for knocked-down or ready-to-assemble cabinets

Figure 4-55 Shelf supports.
(Courtesy of Julius Blum, Inc.)

Leg levelers.   Leg levelers are available to ease the leveling and installation of base cabinets. They are designed to receive a clip-on toe-kick board, so they eliminate the need to construct a cabinet toe-kick base. Most of these leg levelers are made of two parts; a socket, which is attached to each corner of the cabinet at the time of construction, and the leveling leg, which is inserted in the socket and adjusted as necessary at the time of installation. These leg levelers can usually be adjusted with a screwdriver from inside the cabinet. A typical leg leveler is shown in Figure 4-56. There are usually four levelers per cabinet, although some designs allow adjacent cabinets to share levelers.

Installation hardware.   Most of the major hardware manufacturers market hardware for hanging wall cabinets on walls, although many installers just use screws for mounting.

Installation hardware usually consists of an adjustable suspension fitting that is attached to the inside of the cabinet side panel and a metal rail or hooks that are attached to the wall. This system allows for three-dimensional adjustment of the cabinet after installation. A typical system is shown in Figure 4-57.

Miscellaneous frameless cabinet hardware.   The manufacturers of hardware for frameless-style cabinets produce a number of other items that can make cabinetmaking easier or that can improve the end product. There are various caps to cover screws and holes. These are available in colors to match the more popular cabinet materials. There are drawer-front adjusters

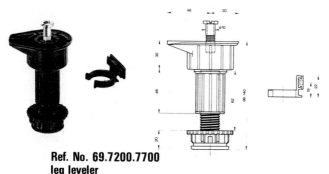

**Ref. No. 69.7200.7700
leg leveler**

Figure 4-56 Leg levelers.
(Courtesy of Julius Blum, Inc.)

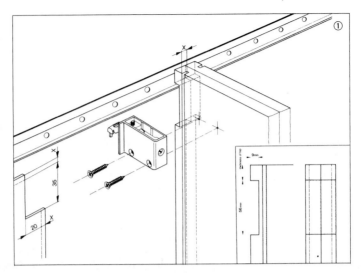

Figure 4-57 Cabinet-installation system. (Courtesy of Julius Blum, Inc.)

that allow drawer fronts to be easily installed and adjusted on the drawer boxes. There are also drawer and door bumper pads to cushion the closing of doors and drawers.

CABINET HARDWARE FOR TRADITIONAL FACE-FRAME CABINETS

Hinges.   Many types and styles of door hinges are available for each of the three basic types of doors described in Chapter 11, namely lip, flush, and overlay. While each of these three basic door types requires a different type of hinge, there are many hinges available for each door type. Hinges may also be classified as surface-mounting hinges, semiconcealed hinges, pivot-pin hinges, and hidden hinges.

Figure 4-58 shows two of the hinges available for lip-type doors. Notice that the semiconcealed type has a step in the door leaf that is designed to fit a 3/8-in. by 3/8-in. rabbet. This hinge is also available in a spring-loaded self-closing type that eliminates the need for door catches.

Figure 4-59 shows two of the hinges available for overlay doors. Notice that the semiconcealed type is very similar to the one used for lip doors, except for the step on the door leaf. These are also available in the self-closing type.

Figure 4-60 shows hinges for flush-fitting doors.

A relatively new hinge that is often used on lip and overlay doors is the demountable type shown in Figure 4-61. Instead of being attached with screws as conventional hinges are, the demountable type is clamped to the cabinet and

Figure 4-58   Hinges for lip-type doors. (Courtesy of Amerock Corporation)

to the door. Mounting this hinge requires a special jig for routing the cabinet face frame and door to accept the hinge clamp, but this hinge has many advantages. Tightening a single screw secures the hinge to the door, and tightening another screw secures the hinge to the cabinet face. The door is then fully adjustable in any direction merely by loosening one or both screws. This allows doors that are slightly warped to hang properly. If the house settles after the cabinets have been set, the doors can easily be readjusted. It also makes it very easy to install cabinets without the doors attached and then install the doors on

Figure 4-59   Hinges for overlay-type doors. (Courtesy of Amerock Corporation)

Figure 4-60   Hinges for flush-fitting doors

the job site. These hinges are also available in single demountable form, in which the cabinet leaf attaches with screws in the conventional manner and the other leaf clamps to the door. This allows the doors to be adjusted side to side and up and down but not in or out from the face of the cabinet.

Figure 4-61   Demountable hinge. (Courtesy of Amerock Corporation)

Pulls.   Drawer and door pulls are available in an almost unlimited number of styles and types. They are usually selected to match the hinge if the hinge is exposed. Some are very ornate, but many of them tend to catch dirt and also the clothing of anyone leaning against the cabinets.

Door catches.   Door catches are available in magnetic or friction types, but they are not needed when self-closing hinges are used. A touch latch is a special latch that releases the door and springs it open when pressure is applied to the outside of the door. This eliminates the need for a door pull. Touch latches are popular on flush-fitting doors where a clean appearance with no exposed hardware is desired.

Drawer guides.   Drawer-guide systems are described in Chapter 12. The hardware used for the shop-built wood center guide usually consists of a set of plastic tabs, as shown in Figure 4-62. These tabs cover all the sliding surfaces to reduce friction and to guide the drawer.

Center under-drawer roller guides are also available. These are shown in Figure 4-63. They usually have a 25-lb. to 35-lb. load capacity.

Figure 4-62 Set of plastic drawer guides

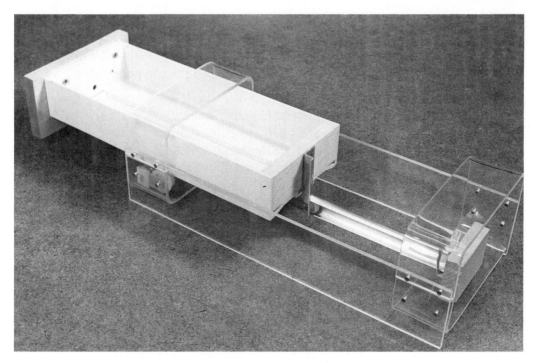

Figure 4-63 Center roller guide

Side roller guides are usually the most desirable (Figure 4-64). They are usually rated at 50-lb. to 75-lb. load capacity and, when properly adjusted, allow the drawer to be moved in or out with very little effort. Most of these require 1/2 in. on either side of the drawer, so in effect they consume 1 in. of available drawer width. These are also available in a full-extension type that allows the drawer to be opened to its full depth.

Side roller guides vary greatly in price, depending on load capacity, smoothness, and other features. They are generally available in 2-in. increments in length.

Adjustable shelf hardware. Adjustable shelves are usually mounted in cabinets with either of two types of hardware. An adjustable shelf standard, such as the one shown in Figure 4-65, may be used along with matching clips. These give incremental 1/2-in. adjustments in height. These standards must be cut in sets of four so that the numbers match on each piece.

The second method of mounting adjustable shelves requires drilling two vertical rows of 1/4-in.-diameter holes in the wall of the cabinet at either end of the shelf (Figure 4-66). These holes are usually drilled on 1-in. centers. The

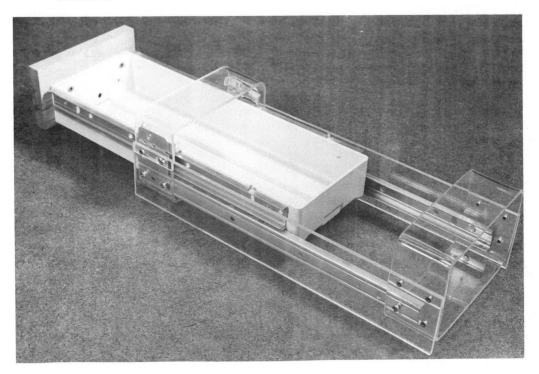

Figure 4-64 Side roller guides

shelf is then supported by inserting a shelf bracket in each of the four holes at the desired height.

Specialty hardware.   There are many other specialty cabinet hardware items that can make cabinets more attractive, more functional, and easier to use. The cabinetmaker should become familiar with catalogs from some of the manufacturers of the hardware. A listing of a few of these hardware items would include pull-out towel racks, false-drawer-front trays, Lazy Susan hardware, swing-up mixer shelves, under-cabinet cookbook shelves, tambour-door guides, sugar and flour dispensers, among many others.

ABRASIVES

Abrasives are used to sand cabinets in preparation for finish and for sanding between coats of finish. In addition, many shops use abrasive planers for sizing wood parts. There are four types of abrasives used on abrasive paper for woodworking: flint, garnet, aluminum oxide, and silicon carbide. These abra-

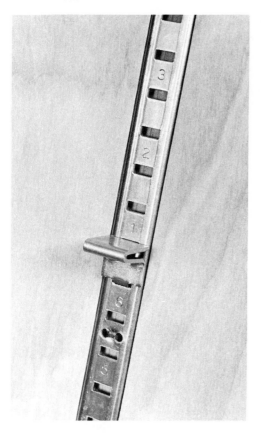

Figure 4-65 Adjustable shelf standard and support clip

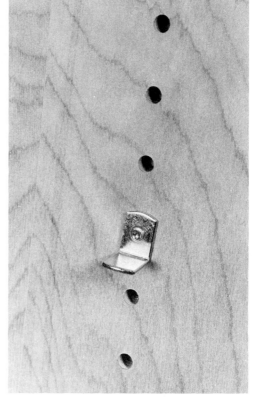

Figure 4-66 Adjustable shelf support

sives are bonded to either a paper or a cloth backing, depending on the intended use of the product.

Flint is the least expensive and the least desirable. It is a relatively soft mineral, and as it wears down, it fractures with fairly dull edges. This makes it cut slowly and wear out fast.

Garnet is a natural stone, reddish brown in color. It is much harder and sharper than flint, and as it is worn down, it fractures with sharp edges that form new cutting surfaces. It is used extensively in woodworking, especially for hand sanding.

Aluminum oxide is a by-product of the aluminum manufacturing industry and is a very hard, sharp abrasive. It stands up well to the heat and loads generated in power sanding and is the abrasive used on almost all sanding belts.

Silicon carbide is slightly softer than aluminum oxide, but it fractures with very sharp edges and is available in very fine grits. It is often mounted on waterproof paper and used in wet-sanding operations. In woodworking it is used primarily for sanding between coats of finish and for some finish sanding on raw wood.

The paper backing for abrasives is available in four weights, designated by the letters A (light) through D (heavy). The grit size is designated by the finest wire-mesh screen through which it will pass. A 60-grit abrasive will just pass through a screen with 60 openings per linear inch, a 240-grit will pass through a screen with 240 openings per linear inch, and so on. Abrasive sheets are further classified as open-coat or closed-coat. Open-coat sheets have less abrasive grit on the sheet. The space between grits is used to carry away the wood fibers removed in the sanding operation. An open-coat abrasive has less tendency to fill up than does a closed-coat abrasive, especially when sanding softwoods. A closed-coat sheet is fully covered with abrasive grit. It has more cutting edges, so it will cut faster and smoother, especially in hardwoods.

Cloth backings are much more suitable than paper backings for machine-sanding operations. Cloth backings are available in X (heavy) and J (light) weights.

CHAPTER 5

Panel Cutting

Accurate panel cutting is absolutely essential when using the frameless cabinet system. The panels must be accurate in size and squareness and must be free of any chipping. How accurate do you have to be? Some sources say that all dimensions must be accurate to within 1/64 in. (.4 mm), but even that much inaccuracy can cause trouble with some assembly systems. The manufacturers of some of the better panel saws guarantee accuracy to 1/10 mm (.004 in.). This is much better.

The need for these extreme accuracy requirements is due in part to the fact that the boring machines used to bore the system holes and the construction holes are indexed from the edges and corners of the panels. With some machines, the front row of system holes is indexed from the front edge of the panel, and the back row from the back edge. The bottom construction holes are indexed from the bottom edge of the panel and the top row from the top edge. If the panels are out of square or not sized accurately, the hole locations for dowel holes or hardware holes will not line up.

Inaccurate or out-of-square parts can cause the final cabinet to be out of square. This means that it will be impossible to fit the doors to the cabinet. On a face-frame cabinet, on the other hand, some degree of out of squareness can be tolerated when overlap doors or lip doors are being used.

On frameless cabinets, if the cabinet bottom and ends are not exactly the same width, there will be a misalignment at the front of the cabinet with no face frame to hide it.

The other major concern on panel cutting for frameless cabinets is to avoid chipping. All the sheet materials normally used in frameless cabinet-making have a tendency to chip along the bottom edge of the cut (for a table saw). Some are more prone to chipping than others, but they will all chip unless precautions are taken.

One of the first concerns for anyone considering adopting the frameless system is to provide a method of obtaining accurate, chip-free panel cutting.

The normal techniques involve the use of a saw with a scoring blade ahead of the main blade and/or the use of special blades designed for these materials. Several saw-blade manufacturers have developed blades with hollow ground teeth designed especially for cutting laminated particle boards.

Scoring blades are small-diameter blades mounted ahead of the main blade. They rotate in the opposite direction and are set to make a shallow cut through the surface of the material before it is cut by the main blade. This keeps the main blade from chipping the surface as the teeth break through from the back of the face laminate.

The scoring blade must be the same thickness as the main blade and must be in perfect alignment with the main blade. There are two popular types of scoring blades. One is made in two halves with shims in between to obtain the desired thickness. The other type is a one-piece design with the teeth tapered narrower at the top. In the latter case, the width of the scoring cut is determined by the depth of blade setting. The one-piece blade is easier to adjust for kerf width, but unfortunately, if the panel that is being cut does not lay perfectly flat on the saw table, the scoring cut will be narrow in areas where the panel was not in contact with the table. The scoring cut will not prevent chipping in this area.

PANEL CUTTING FOR THE SMALL SHOP

The minimum recommended saw for panel cutting is a table saw with sliding table and scoring, as shown in Figure 5-1. However, even these saws are quite expensive for a very small shop. A number of smaller shops have been successful using a good quality table saw with a very good fence or one of the after-market fences. In this case, the accuracy is very dependent on the saw operator. Adequate accuracy can be obtained only with a very careful and skilled saw operator.

The problem of chipping must also be overcome when using a standard

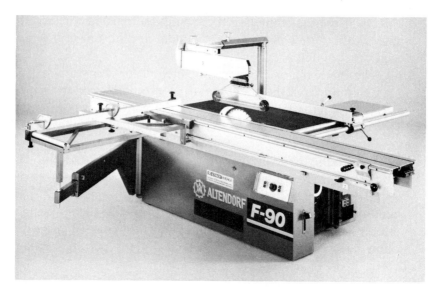

Figure 5-1 Table saw with sliding table and scoring. (Courtesy of Stiles Machinery Inc.)

table saw. The special saw blades previously described show promise in this area. It is also possible to prescore the material by setting the saw blade to protrude above the table by 1/16 in., making a scoring cut across the sheet, then raising the blade to the normal height and completing the cut before moving the fence. This method is effective, but it doubles the time required to cut out a job. The scoring operation can be omitted on cuts where both sides of the cut don't have to be chip free.

The sliding table saws can provide great accuracy and chip-free cuts. They are designed to cut a 4-ft. by 8-ft. sheet in either direction. Some will cut 10-ft. sheets. The scoring blade prevents chipping on the underside of the cut. Note that the scoring blade must be accurately aligned with the main blade. Most of them can also be used for angle cuts, making them more versatile than other panel saws.

The main disadvantages compared with a vertical panel saw are that sliding table saws generally take two people to place the sheet on the saw, and they take up considerably more floor space.

Sliding table saws are generally less expensive than vertical panel saws, although there is some overlapping in price between the best sliding table saws and the least expensive vertical saws.

Shops that cannot afford a good panel-cutting saw may want to explore the option of having panel parts precut. Some material suppliers have panel-cutting services available for a reasonable price. Most shops use standard sizes for cabinet ends, partitions, and other parts. These can be ordered cut to size.

In addition to being cut accurately and chip free, they can save the cabinet shop time in completing jobs, and they may be easier to store than 4-ft. by 8-ft. sheets.

PANEL CUTTING FOR THE MEDIUM-SIZE SHOP

Vertical panel saws (Figure 5-2) are a popular choice for medium-size shops. They are capable of great accuracy and squareness. They take up relatively little floor space, and they can be loaded by one person. Many of them will cut multiple sheets at once.

They may or may not be equipped with scoring blades. If they do not have scoring blades, there should be some other provision to assure chip-free cutting.

Some models use the main blade to score the sheet by making a scoring pass in the opposite direction before making the main cut in the normal direction.

The price range for vertical panel saws starts near the top of the sliding table range and goes up from there. There are many options available, including automatic (power) feed and electronic digital readouts that give cutting measurement to .1 mm.

Many vertical panel saws are designed to make either vertical or horizontal cuts. These are called two-way vertical saws. Such a saw is shown in

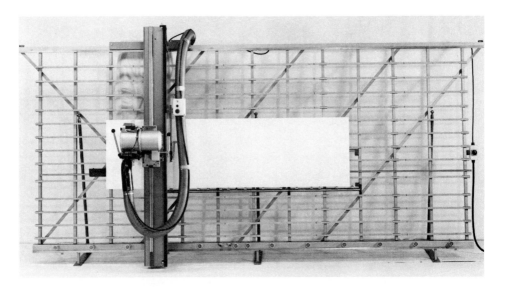

Figure 5-2 Vertical panel-cutting saw. (Courtesy of Colonial Saw)

Figure 5-3. The sheet is placed on the saw in a horizontal position. Vertical cuts are made by moving the panel against preset stops or by moving the saw guide arm to another position. Horizontal cuts are made by turning the saw blade to a horizontal position and by feeding the saw manually unless the machine is an automatic-feed model. When making horizontal cuts, it is necessary to have someone hold the top piece being cut to prevent it from dropping down and pinching the blade. As an alternative, wedges can be used in the saw kerf to achieve the same purpose.

Some of these saws also require periodic replacement of the wood or plastic cleats that support the panel because these are cut in the process of cutting the panels.

The other panel saw is the vertical-only model, such as the one shown in Figure 5-4. On this type of saw, the saw always travels in the same path, so the material is moved into position against preset stops. The sheet must be turned to alternate between lengthwise cuts and crosscuts. Because of the fact that the blade always travels in the same path, it is somewhat easier to guard the blade and provide a dust-collection system with this type of saw.

The main advantages of each type are summarized as follows:

- Two-way vertical saws:
  - The panel has to be handled less.
  - Some models can do plunge cutting.
- One-way vertical saws:
  - No provision has to be made to keep the wood from pinching the blade.

Figure 5-3 Two-way vertical panel-cutting saw. (Courtesy of Colonial Saw)

Figure 5-4 Vertical-only panel-cutting saw. (Courtesy of Hendricksaw)

- There are no panel-support rails that need to be replaced periodically.
- The blade-guarding system is often better.

Either type of vertical panel cutting can usually be operated by one person.

PANEL CUTTING FOR THE LARGE SHOP

The level of sophistication and automation available in panel cutting for the large production shop is truly amazing. The saws used are nearly always some variation of a horizontal-beam type of saw. Some are available with automatic loading and unloading features, and many will cut multiple sheets at one time. Many are computer controlled, and some can directly use the cutting plans generated by panel-optimization programs, as described in Chapter 15.

The simplest of these saws requires two people to set the panels on the saw. The operator then pushes the panel against an electronically or mechanically set stop to index the panel for cutting. After the cut is made, the second person removes the part or returns it to the crosscutting area. Figure 5-5 shows a manually fed saw that requires two operators.

The next step up adds an automatic pusher to the saw, allowing one-person operation. The pusher pushes one or more sheets into cutting position. These machines are also often equipped with microprocessor-controlled programs so that all the items on a cutting list will automatically be cut without requiring setup changes on the part of the operator.

These saws may be used for both ripping and crosscutting or for ripping only, when used in conjunction with a crosscutting saw. Figures 5-6 and 5-7 show these two arrangements. Using two saws, as in Figure 5-7, allows both ripping and crosscutting to occur simultaneously, thus increasing production.

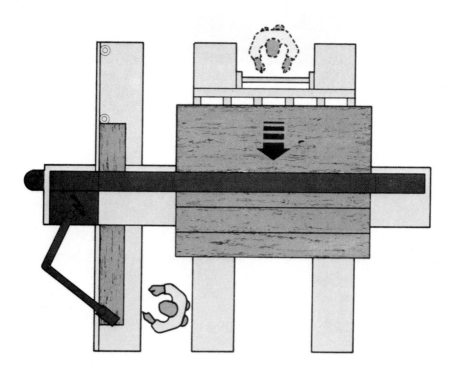

Figure 5-5 Manually fed beam-type panel saw. (Courtesy of SCMI Corporation)

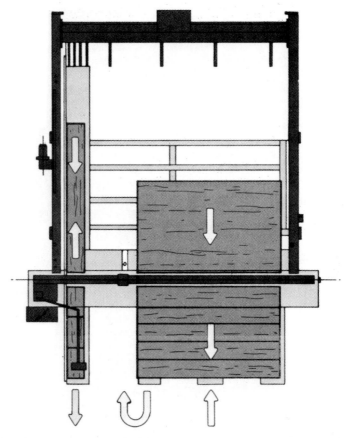

Figure 5-6 One possible cutting arrangement. (Courtesy of SCMI Corporation)

Some of these machines can be equipped with loading platforms allowing stacks of material to be loaded with forklifts.

Figure 5-8 shows a saw equipped with a pusher that permits single-person operation.

Perhaps the ultimate panel-cutting saw for the large production shop would be an angular saw that includes a beam-mounted saw for ripping panels and a second beam-mounted crosscut saw at 90° to the ripping saw. Full computer programming and automatic loading and unloading are often incorporated in these saws. This makes it possible to load stacks of material in the saw with a forklift. The automatic pusher then pushes multiple sheets into position to be rip-cut as determined by the computer program. After the first rip cut has been made, another automatic pusher pushes them into position to be crosscut at the crosscutting station. Figure 5-9 shows an angular panel saw.

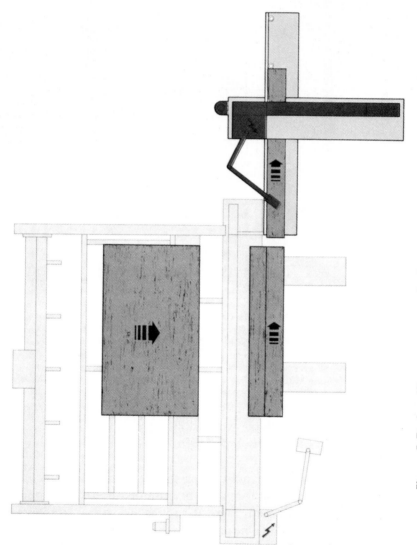

Figure 5-7 A cutting arrangement using a second saw for crosscutting. (Courtesy of SCMI Corporation)

Figure 5-8 Saw equipped with a pusher, permitting one-person operation. (Courtesy of SCMI Corporation)

Figure 5-9 Angular panel saw. (Courtesy of Stiles Machinery Inc.)

CHAPTER 6

Edge Banding

Edge banding is one of the main operations in any frameless cabinetmaking operation. Since there are no face frames to cover the fronts of the cabinet boxes, it is necessary to band the front edges of the cabinet boxes. Doors, drawer fronts, and shelves are also edge-banded. Edge-banding material is most often a thin plastic (PVC, polyester, or melamine) that matches the color of the sheet material being used. However, thick PVC edge banding may also be used with accent colors or to allow radius-cut edges. Wood veneer, thicker wood strips, or plastic-laminate strips may also be used. Some edge banders will apply any of these materials, while others may be used only with thin materials. Some edge banders are capable of soft forming or post forming to produce contour molded edges.

EDGE BANDING FOR THE SMALL SHOP

There are many options for applying edge banding in small quantities. Some of them, however, are quite labor intensive and should be considered only when there is a very small amount of banding to be done. Examples of labor-intensive methods include applying edge banding with contact cement or applying preglued edge banding with a clothes iron. While these methods require a negligible investment in equipment, they are so slow that they are not practical in production situations. They are, however, sometimes used to apply edge banding to parts that cannot be banded with an edge bander. These might include parts that are too small, too large, or of a shape that would prevent them from being banded with a conventional bander.

Benchtop hot-platen banders are a relatively inexpensive option for the small shop doing a limited amount of banding. Two of these benchtop banders are shown in Figure 6-1. They are easy to operate and maintain and, with some materials, allow the banding of all four sides of a panel in one operation. They also allow banding of contoured edges. Their low initial cost is offset somewhat by the fact that they require the use of preglued edge banding and the fact that they cannot use the less expensive PVC edge banding because the heat of the heating platen is too great for PVC and other thermoplastic materials. But they can be used with wood veneers in coil form, with polyester, and with melamine.

Hot-air edge banders are another edge-banding option. They are available in benchtop or floor models (Figure 6-2). They also require a preglued edge banding, but they use a jet of hot air to melt the adhesive rather than a heating platen. This doesn't get the banding material itself as hot as the hot-platen model does, so it allows the use of preglued PVC edge banding as well as polyester, melamine, and wood. Some models will do contour banding

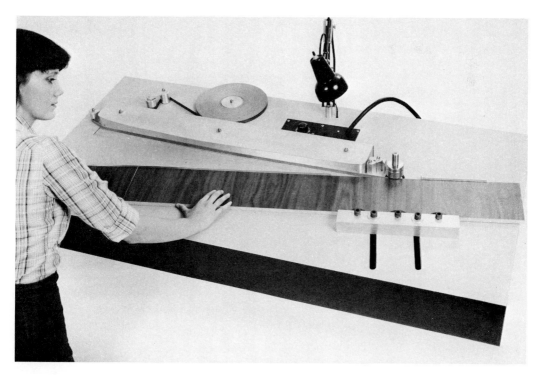

Figure 6-1 Hot-platen edge banders. (Courtesy of Woodtape Inc.)

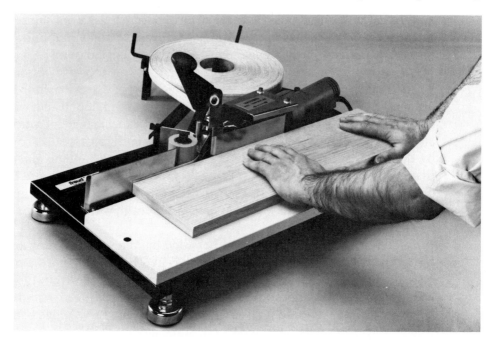

(a)

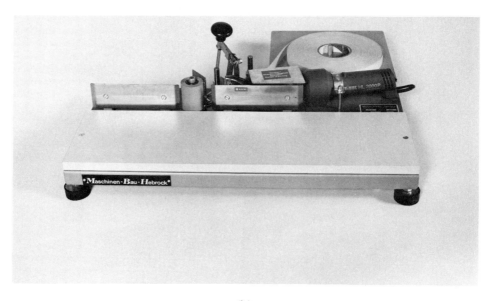

(b)

Figure 6-2   Hot-air edge banders ((a) Freud, (b,c,d) Therm O Web)

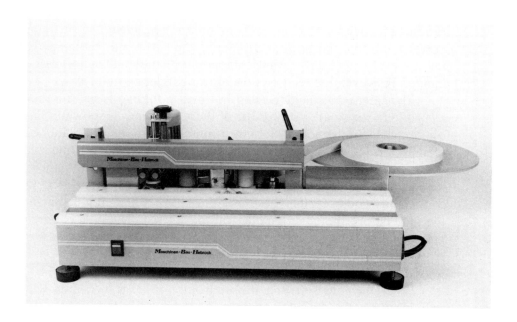

(c)

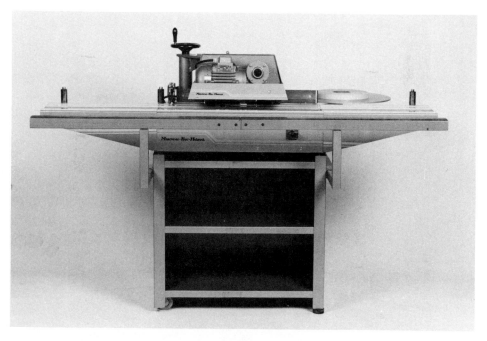

(d)

as well as straight edges. Some of these hot-air banders approach the smaller-production edge banders in levels of automation, including such features as power feed, top and bottom trimming, and flush-end trimming. They also feature a very rapid startup time compared with the smaller, hot-melt adhesive bander. However, the feed rate on hot-air banders is quite slow.

The mini edge bander using hot-melt adhesive is yet another option available to the smaller shop. One of these machines is shown in Figure 6-3. These machines are somewhat more complex than the hot-platen or hot-air models, but they do allow the use of non-preglued edge bandings as well as the use of thin wood strips and plastic-laminate strips. The panels are fed manually, so some skill on the part of the operator is required to obtain consistently good results. These machines have a heated gluepot that melts the glue before the edge banding can be started. The glue is purchased in granular form. The glue remaining in the gluepot after the edge-banding run is completed will solidify but can be melted again the next time the machine is used.

When the glue is melted, the application roller is turned on. The glue is fed onto the roller from the gluepot. As the panel is fed past the roller, the glue is applied to the panel edge. The edge-banding material is then applied

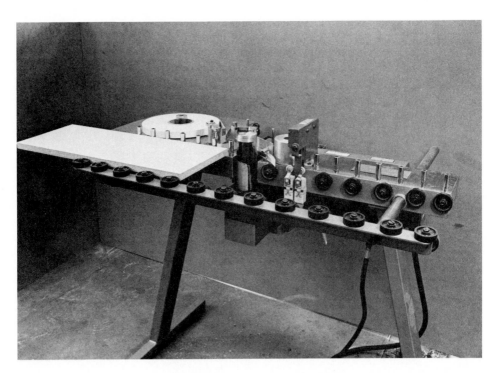

Figure 6-3 Mini edge bander

Figure 6-4   Automatic end trimmer

as the panel is fed past a pressure roller. The glue spread rate can be adjusted for different substrate materials. For example, a very porous particle board may require a heavy spread while a medium-density fiberboard may require a much lighter spread.

These mini edge banders usually do not have edge- or end-trimming features, so this requires another operation after the banding has been applied. The ends may be trimmed with an automatic end trimmer such as the one shown in Figure 6-4. The edges may be trimmed with a hand-held trimmer such as the one shown in Figure 6-5. A portable router or laminate trimmer may also be used. Trimming is usually followed by a light filing to ease the sharp edges and to make sure that the edge banding is flush with the panel surface.

EDGE BANDING FOR THE LARGER SHOP

Selecting an edge bander for a larger shop can be an intimidating task. To begin with, there are many materials used for edge banding, including thin

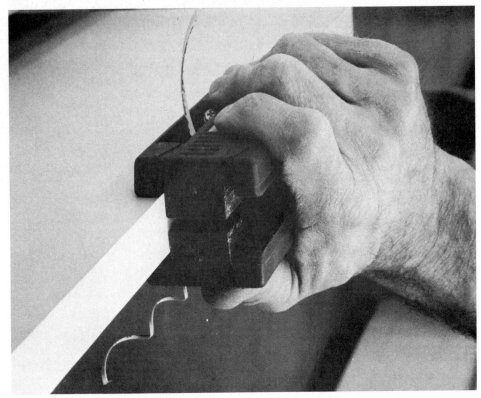

Figure 6-5   Hand edge trimmer for PVC banding

synthetic materials such as PVC, melamine, and polyester. There is also thick PVC in solid or multicolors. There is also thin wood edge banding in continuous coils, thin wood strips, and wood boards up to 1 in. or more in thickness. High-pressure plastic laminates are also used as edge banding. While it is possible to purchase a machine that is capable of applying all these materials, it may be more cost effective to purchase several smaller machines if it is necessary to run a variety of materials.

Edge banders are made up of a series of stations, each designed to perform a specific operation on the banded panel. There may be stations for end trimming, edge trimming, radius milling for thick edge bandings, scraping, reheating, sanding, buffing, and milling for thick wood edges. A machine designed to apply all materials would, then, need to have many stations, some of which are not being used at any given time. It may also take considerable setup time to change from one banding material to another, or from one panel thickness to another. Since an edge bander can cost from $15,000 up to several hundred thousand dollars, it represents an important decision. Some larger automatic edge banders are shown in Figure 6-6.

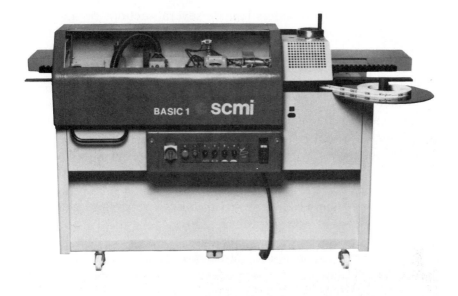

(a)

(b)

(c)

Figure 6-6 Large production edge banders. (Courtesy of SCMI Corporation)

Automatic edge banders include several sections or stations. The first one is the *magazine section*, which usually has provision for coil feeding and strip feeding. On some machines, this section can tilt to band a beveled edge.

The second section is the *gluing section*, which includes the gluepot and application roller(s) or an extrusion system for applying glue. Systems using a hot-melt gluepot may take from 15 to 45 min. heat-up time before the machine can be used. Machines with extrusion systems require only 2 to 3 min. initial heat-up time.

The adhesive may be applied to the substrate, the edge banding, or both. When using PVA glue with thick wood banding, it is common to apply glue to both surfaces.

The third section is the *pressure section*, in which the edge-band material is pressed tightly against the substrate. This step is critical in obtaining a sound joint with a thin glue line. If hot-melt glues are being used, the pressure section must be very close to the glue section to avoid allowing the glue to cool before the banding is applied to the substrate. (It is also important that the panel, material, edge banding, and shop air temperature all be above 60°F.) Many edge-banding problems have been traced to allowing the glue to cool before the bond was completed.

The fourth section is the *trimming section*. This section may consist only of end-trimming saws and flush-edge trimming cutters, or it may also include heads for making corner radius cuts on thick banding, and for contour form trimming.

The fifth section, the *finishing section*, is used for scraping, sanding and buffing. If thick PVC edge banding is being radius-cut, the resulting mill marks must be removed, so a scraping knife is usually added. The scraping operation will discolor some PVC colors so a small heater is used to slightly soften the edge and bring back the color. The scraping knives may also be used to remove excess glue.

Sanding heads may be included for sanding wood edge banding, and buffing heads may be included for buffing the edges of plastic edge-banding materials to remove final traces of glue. As you can see, these machines can be quite complex!

Since the edge bander is a critical part of the frameless cabinet system and since this equipment is very expensive, it is important that the right edge bander be selected.

One of the most important considerations in purchasing an edge bander is to purchase it from a dealer that is capable of providing setup and operator-training services. The dealer should also carry a supply of critical spare parts to prevent excessive down time in the event of a machine breakdown. These larger edge banders are quite complex and the setup for each material must be just right to get high-quality results. Operator training is very important and will enable you to get the result that the machine is capable of. Operator training should also include training on routine maintenance. A knowledgeable dealer can be very helpful in trouble-shooting problems with edge banders.

Another important consideration is to analyze what kind of edge banding you will be doing most and choose a machine that works well with that material. For example, if you use only PVC edge banding, there is no need to pay for the capability to apply thick wood board edge banding. Again, a knowledgeable dealer can be a big help in selecting the best edge bander for the job.

Another important consideration is the amount of time required to change from one banding material to another or to change from one panel thickness to another. With so many banding materials available, it is more important to be able to change quickly than it was when thin PVC was the only material being used extensively. Many shops are finding that in order to accommodate varied customer preferences, they are running short batches of one or two jobs with one material and then switching to another, rather than running one material continuously. Some shops also change glue colors for different materials, so ease of cleaning the gluepot should be considered.

Some machines can be changed over from one material to another in a very few minutes while changing others is a major operation. If several materials are being used in equal quantities, it may be better to consider purchasing several smaller banders, each dedicated to a specific material, rather than one large bander with multiple-material capability. This is especially true if there is enough volume to keep more than one machine busy.

Other factors to look at would include the length of heat-up time required to get the glue up to working temperature, feeding speed, ease of cleaning and maintenance, and the maximum- and minimum-size panels that can be accommodated.

COMMON EDGE-BANDING PROBLEMS

Some edge-banding problems are actually panel problems. The panel must be warm (60°F minimum), free of dust, must be at 8% to 9% moisture content, and must have a perfectly square-cut edge. If the panel edge is even slightly beveled, the pressure rollers will apply pressure only to the high edge, leaving a thick, weak glue joint that will almost certainly fail.

Cleanliness is also very important. If glue is allowed to build up on the sides of the gluepot, it will act as an insulator and give false temperature readings. A good dust-collection system is also essential to collect trimmings. PVC materials are especially troublesome in this regard because of static attraction to various parts of the machine. They must not be allowed to accumulate in the machine.

Temperature for hot-melt adhesives is also very critical and must be carefully monitored. Some machines have thermostats in the gluepot and on the glue-spreading roller. However, if the panel is cold or if the room air temperature is cold enough to chill the glue before the pressure is applied to the banding, failure will occur. Normal room temperatures must be maintained, and edge banders should not be located near outside-opening doors where a blast of cold winter air could chill the glue.

The thickness of the glue film must be adjusted for the substrate being used. A panel made of relatively coarse chips will require more glue than one composed of more highly compressed, fine chips.

CHAPTER 7

Boring

The frameless cabinetmaking system depends on a series of accurately located holes in the cabinet sides for the installation of hardware for doors, drawers, shelves, and other applications. Many cabinet manufacturers also use holes for dowel assembly or for the installation of KD fittings. Holes are also bored in cabinet doors for the frameless system hinges. Other boring applications may include boring drawer fronts for attachment hardware and boring drawer parts for dowel assembly. See Chapter 2 for a discussion of the system holes and construction holes.

The equipment for boring these holes can range from attachments for small drill presses, to automatic multispindle boring machines, to computer-controlled point-to-point boring machines The main requirements are that the holes be very accurately located and that they have no chipping around the perimeter.

There are multipurpose machines available that can bore system holes, construction holes, and door-hinge holes by changing the setup on the machine. Other shops use one or more special-purpose machines for each of these operations.

BORING FOR THE SMALL SHOP

Smaller shops often use a system other than dowels for assembling cabinet boxes. They may use one of the plate-jointing systems, or they may use the special particle-board screws designed for this purpose.

If dowels are not used for cabinet assembly, the need for a machine to bore construction holes or the need for a dual-purpose machine is eliminated. A machine for boring system holes (5-mm holes, 32 mm center to center) will be needed as will a machine for boring doors for hinges. Drawer-boring machines may also be used.

The least expensive system for boring system holes is probably a multi-spindle attachment for a standard drill press (Figure 7-1). These usually consist of 5-, 7-, or 9-counter rotating spindles equipped with 5-mm bits. There is usually a pin stop at each end that can be engaged in the last hole of the previously drilled set to allow drilling long rows of system holes. A guide fence with adjustable stops may be incorporated to index the first hole from the top or bottom of a panel.

There are also drill-press attachments for boring doors to accept hinges (Figure 7-2). They often incorporate a system for pressing a hinge into the door after the boring operation. These drill-press attachments are usually marketed by the distributors of various brands of frameless cabinet hardware.

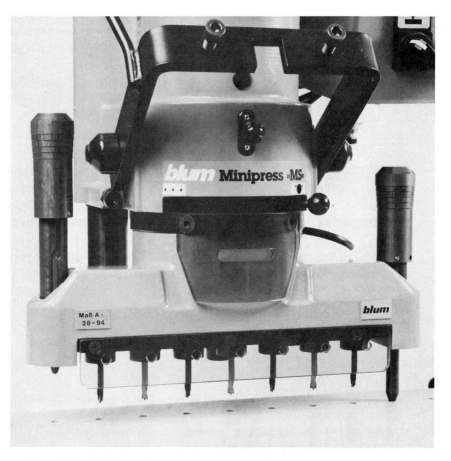

Figure 7-1 Multispindle drill-press attachment for boring system holes

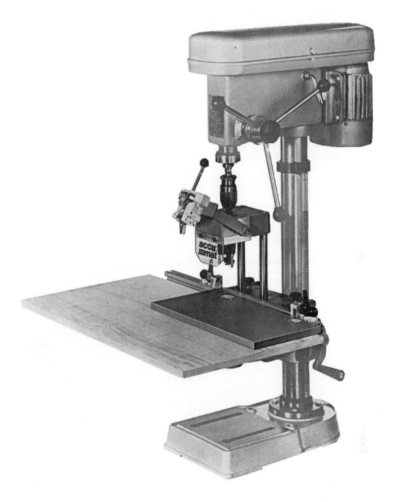

Figure 7-2 Drill-press attachment for boring hinge holes. (Courtesy of Mepla Inc., Furniture Fittings)

The next step up would probably be one of the "minipresses" marketed by the frameless system hardware manufacturers as well as by some machinery manufacturers. These are generally faster, more accurate, and easier to operate than the drill-press attachment. They often have pneumatic stock hold-downs, pneumatic boring stroke, and easily adjustable stops and fences with detent for standard boring setbacks. Figures 7-3 and 7-4 show two such presses. These machines usually have easily interchangeable heads for system boring and for boring hinge holes. Many shops that have larger machines for boring system holes keep a minipress setup for boring hinge holes and pressing hinges into place.

Figure 7-3 Minipress for boring system holes and hinge holes

It should be noted that the location of the screw holes in relation to the cup hole is different with each of the major hinge manufacturers, so once you buy a hinge-boring machine, you are "locked in" with that brand of hinge.

It is best to compare brands of hardware for features that you need for your cabinet, then make sure there is a good, reliable vendor for that brand in your area before selecting a hinge-boring machine. Figures 7-5, 7-6, and 7-7 show a minipress being used to bore system holes, bore hinge holes, and press a hinge into a door.

BORING FOR THE MEDIUM TO LARGE SHOP

The next step up gets more complicated. There are machines that will drill one row of system holes, machines that will drill both rows of system holes,

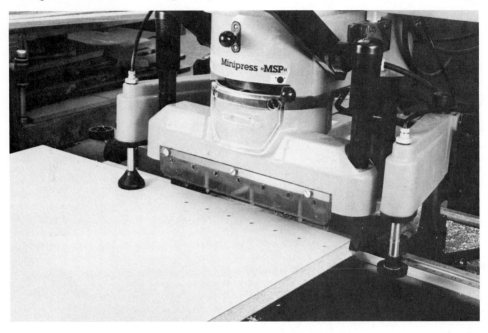

Figure 7-4   Minipress setup for boring system holes.

Figure 7-5   Boring system holes with a minipress

Figure 7-6   Boring door holes with a minipress

Figure 7-7   Pressing a hinge into a door

machines that will drill horizontal construction holes, and machines that will drill vertical construction holes. There are combination machines that will drill both system holes and construction holes and yet others that will do just vertical and horizontal construction holes. As with any combination machine, a combination boring machine will usually cost less than comparable individual machines and will take up less space in the shop. Figures 7-8 and 7-9 show two high-quality combination boring machines. The down side, of course, is that these combination machines require a certain amount of time to be changed from one operation to the other. On some of the

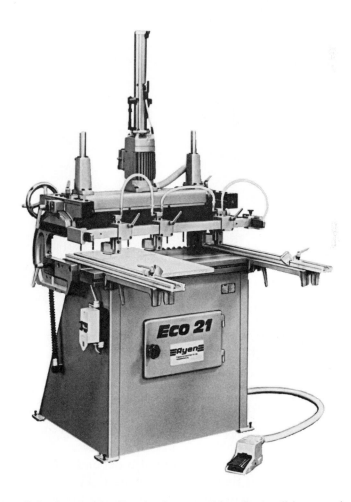

Figure 7-8 A combination boring machine that will bore system holes, construction (dowel) holes, and holes for KD fittings. (Courtesy of Force Machinery, Inc.)

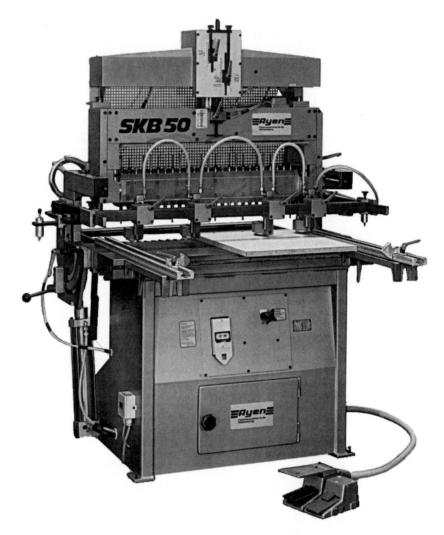

Figure 7-9   A very versatile combination boring machine. (Courtesy of Force Machinery, Inc.)

better machines, this changeover can be accomplished quite quickly, but it will never be as fast as having an individual machine setup for each operation.

The choice of machines will also depend somewhat on the volume of work to be done. If there is enough work to keep two boring machines busy, it would make sense to have a system hole-boring machine and a construction hole-boring machine rather than two combination machines (Figures 7-10, 7-11, and 7-12).

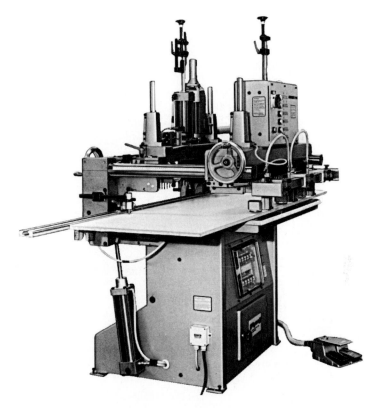

Figure 7-10 A boring machine that will bore both rows of system holes in one operation. (Courtesy of Force Machinery, Inc.)

The next step up in boring machines is a computer numerical-control (CNC) or point-to-point machine (Figure 7-13). The machines in this category that are designed for frameless cabinet construction usually consist of one or more line-boring heads, a head for boring individual holes such as construction holes, and a routing head for cutting grooves and other machining.

The machine is programmed in advance for the work that is to be performed on each panel. For example, a cabinet end panel might have system holes bored, dowel assembly holes bored, a groove machined for the cabinet back, and a curved groove routed for a roll-top door before the part is removed from the machine. The next part in the machine might be the opposite end of the cabinet, which requires the same machining operations, but done as a mirror image. The next part may be something entirely different. Once the programming is done, there is no changeover time required to run different parts.

Figure 7-11 A boring machine that will bore both horizontal and vertical construction holes. (Courtesy of Ritter Manufacturing Inc.)

These machines are very expensive, but they are ideally suited for shops doing a wide variety of work because of their versatility and near instantaneous changeover between running different parts.

The programming of these machines has become easier in recent years with advances in computer technology. Many machines feature the ability to run mirror-image programs without reprogramming. Some allow one program to be run while another is being loaded or edited. Some allow easy additions to standard programs such as machining for a special piece of hardware. Some allow common hardware-boring patterns to be programmed as preset modules so the program can be told where a certain hardware application is to be and it will bore all the necessary holes in the correct locations.

Figure 7-12   A single-line, system hole-boring machine. (Courtesy of Ritter Manufacturing Inc.)

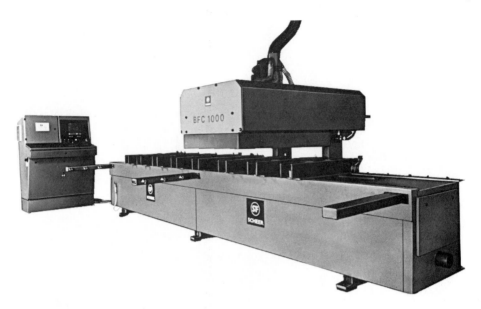

Figure 7-13 A computer numerical control (CNC) point-to-point boring machine

CHAPTER 8

Frameless Cabinet Assembly

One of the major differences between the frameless cabinet system and the conventional face-frame cabinet system is in the method of assembling the cabinet. Traditional face-frame cabinets are assembled with dado and rabbet joints. Frameless cabinets are assembled with butt joints. The butt joints are always reinforced in some way. Most larger-production shops use wood dowel as the reinforcing medium. Knock-down (KD) hardware may be used for ready-to-assemble (RTA) cabinets. Smaller shops may use screws or plate joints as the reinforcing medium.

SCREW ASSEMBLY

Screw assembly is a popular choice for many smaller shops since it eliminates the need for a case clamp and a machine for boring construction holes. The screws used are a special thick screw with deep threads, especially designed for use in particle board (Figure 8-1). The drawbacks of screw assembly are that it is somewhat slower and the fact that screw heads are exposed on finished ends.

The slower construction is a result of having to clamp mating parts together while drilling pilot holes for screws and then driving the screws. Special drill attachments are available to ensure that the hole is drilled perpendicular to the surface and in the proper location. Multiple-spindle

Figure 8-1 Cabinet assembly screw for particle board

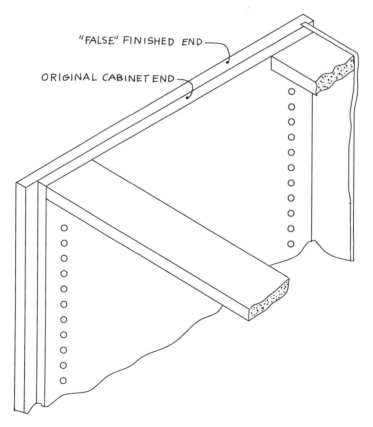

"FALSE" FINISHED END

ORIGINAL CABINET END

Figure 8-2 "False" finished end used to cover assembly screw heads on cabinet ends

boring machines can be used to bore pilot holes for screws, but the purchase of such a machine would eliminate part of the initial cost advantage of using screws for assembly.

The slower assembly time required for screwing cabinets together is offset by the savings in equipment required for dowel assembly.

The problem of exposed screw heads on cabinet finished ends is more difficult. There are caps that can be snapped to the screw heads to cover them. These are color-matched to the popular cabinet boards. These plugs are visible and may not be acceptable in all situations.

Some shops have overcome this problem by making the finished end panel of a one-sided laminate, leaving the particle-board side to the outside. A vertical grade, high-pressure plastic-laminate sheet is then laminated to the cabinet end after assembly, thus covering the exposed screw heads.

Yet other shops attach a second finished end to the cabinet (using screws from inside the cabinet). This second finished end is wider than the original cabinet end and extends flush with the front surface of the cabinet doors or drawers (Figure 8-2). This second finished end can also cover an exposed edge of a cabinet back, allowing the back to be stapled directly to the back of the other cabinet rather than being set in a rabbet or groove.

PLATE JOINT ASSEMBLY

Plate jointing (sometimes called wafer or biscuit jointing) is another popular assembly option for the smaller shop. A special machine (Figure 8-3) is used to machine a semielliptical slot in the parts to be joined. Small wood plates (Figure 8-4) are used as reinforcing splines. These plates are compressed approximately 20%. When they are glued into the slot, the moisture in the glue causes them to expand, making a very tight joint.

Compared with screw assembly, plate joint assembly has the advantage of being completely hidden. Its disadvantage is that the parts must remain clamped until the glue is at least partially cured. Another disadvantage compared with dowel assembly is that plate joint assembly provides accurate part location in only one direction. When used for cabinet assembly, it will not, for example, keep the front edge of a cabinet bottom flush with the front edge of a cabinet end. Therefore, the person assembling the cabinet must be very careful to make sure that all front surfaces are flush when the cabinet is clamped together. However, plate joint assembly is so much faster than hand doweling that it has become very popular.

The following sequence of photographs shows the machining required to assemble a typical cabinet using the plate-jointing system. Figure 8-5 shows the slots being machined in a cabinet end, using pencil marks as guides. Figure

Figure 8-3   Plate-jointing machine. (Courtesy of Colonial Saw)

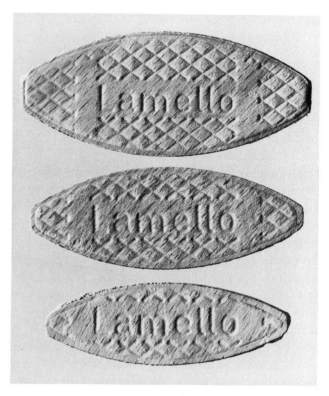

Figure 8-4   Wood plates for plate-jointing system. (Courtesy of Colonial Saw)

Figure 8-5 Machining slots in a cabinet end for plate-jointing system, using pencil marks as guides

8-6 shows matching slots being machined in the cabinet bottom. The cabinet end and bottom are held together for marking the location of the slots. Figure 8-7 shows the machining of slots to attach a partition to a cabinet bottom. Note that the partition is clamped to the cabinet bottom as a guide. Figure 8-8 shows

Figure 8-6 Machining slots in the cabinet bottom

Figure 8-7   Machining slots for a cabinet partition

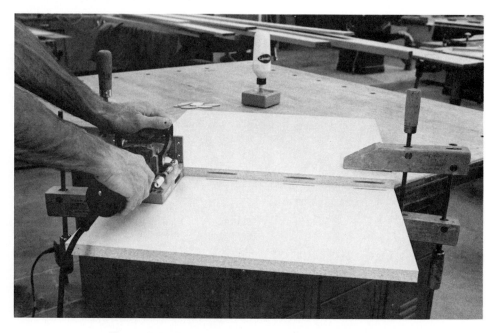

Figure 8-8   Slots being machined in the partition

Figure 8-9　Assembling cabinet parts with plates in place

a matching slot being machined in the partition. Figure 8-9 shows the parts being assembled with the plates in place.

These plates are available in three different sizes suitable for joining materials as thin as 7/16 in. up to 1 in. or more.

DOWEL ASSEMBLY

Dowel assembly is the choice of the majority of large production shops because of the rapid assembly it permits, its accuracy, and its strength. To fully realize all the benefits of dowel assembly, it is necessary to have an accurate and efficient system for boring the construction holes, a dowel-inserter machine, and a case clamp for final assembly. Since these three machines represent a minimum investment of $25,000, it is easy to see why the dowel assembly system is not often used in small shops.

Construction dowel holes are usually 8 mm in diameter and are usually 38 mm (1 1/2 in.) long. The dowels should be as deep as possible into the cabinet end, maintaining a 4-mm end clearance (Figure 8-10). Dowel-boring machines are discussed in Chapter 8, and boring patterns are discussed in

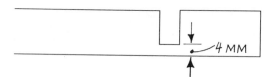

Figure 8-10 A 4-mm end clearance should be maintained for dowel hole depths.

Figure 8-11 An automatic dowel inserter. (Courtesy of Force Machinery Co.)

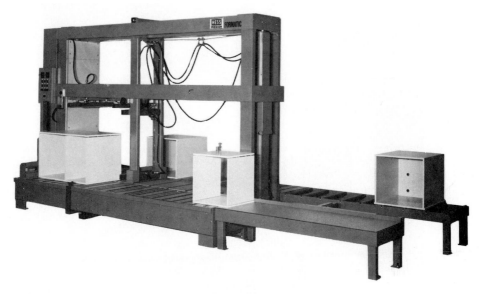

Figure 8-12 A cabinet case clamp. (Courtesy of Force Machinery Co.)

Chapter 2. The most important consideration is that dowel holes be accurately located to ensure that the cabinet parts line up properly during assembly.

High production rates require the use of a dowel inserter (Figure 8-11). They automatically inject a measured amount of glue into each dowel hole and then insert the dowel. Some of the better ones automatically check the length and diameter of the dowels to prevent driving an oversize dowel and splitting the panel.

After the dowels are inserted, the cabinet box is assembled and placed in a case clamp (Figure 8-12). Case clamps have the advantage of applying pressure uniformly, ensuring a square cabinet. Many of them can clamp multiple cabinets at once. Some require manual adjustment for cabinet sizes, some can be programmed for cabinet size, and some are automatic. Some even have an automatic-feed feature that feeds the assembled cabinet into the clamping areas and then out to a conveyor system after clamping. Most machines have a timer to set the clamping time.

READY-TO-ASSEMBLE CABINETS

The development of the frameless cabinet system has revived interest in making knocked-down or ready-to-assemble cabinets. The modular construction system makes it very convenient to install hardware that permits easy on-the-job assembly. This offers many advantages to the manufacturer. It

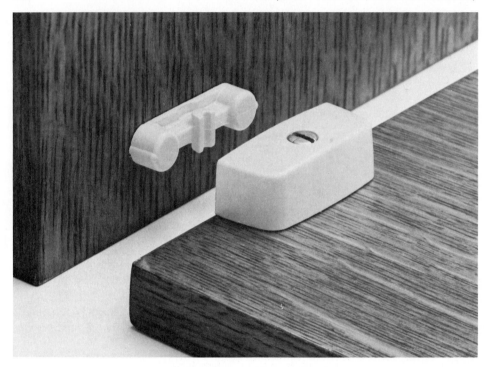

Figure 8-13   KD or RTA assembly fittings

obviously saves the time that would have been spent in assembling the cabinet, and it eliminates the need for case clamps. (A dowel inserter may still be needed because dowels are often used in conjunction with KD fittings.)

It is much cheaper to ship cabinets in knocked-down form than assembled because of the reduction in bulk. Warehousing costs and packaging costs will be far less for the same reason. It is also often easier to move cabinets to their final location if they are not assembled.

Each manufacturer of frameless system hardware offers one or more ready-to-assemble hardware systems. Most of these systems allow final assembly with only a screwdriver.

Each manufacturer's assembly fittings require different drilling patterns, but these can usually be accomplished with standard boring machines. Many of the assembly-fitting systems also use dowels for alignment. Figure 8-13 shows a KD assembly fitting.

CHAPTER 9

Doors and Drawers
for Frameless Cabinets

DOOR AND DRAWER HEIGHTS

Before beginning our discussion of doors and drawer construction, it is important to note that door and drawer heights must be consistent with the 32-mm hole system being used, as described in Chapter 2. If the cabinet heights are in multiples of 32 mm, then the drawer and door heights will also be in 32-mm multiples.

DOOR AND DRAWER-FRONT MATERIAL

One of the most popular door and drawer-front materials for frameless cabinets is plastic-laminate-clad particle board. This is available prelaminated in either 3/4-in. or 5/8-in. thicknesses in a wide range of colors. Vertical grade (1/32 in. thick) plastic laminate is usually used for this application. This makes a very attractive and durable door that requires little or no maintenance and is easy to clean.

This material may be edge banded with PVC, polyester, or melamine plastic-laminate strips, or with wood strips. Polyester or melamine-laminated particle board is also sometimes used for doors and drawer fronts. It is considerably less expensive than plastic laminates, but is not as durable. It is considered suitable for light-duty applications. The same options for edge banding are available.

For cabinets where a more traditional appearance is desired, frame-and-panel doors, as described in Chapter 11, may be used. Glass doors using a wood frame may be used in the same way.

Hardwood plywood with matching wood edge banding may also be used.

FITTING OPTIONS

Doors and drawer fronts may be fitted to the cabinet in one of three ways: full overlay, in which the door or drawer front covers the entire front edge of the

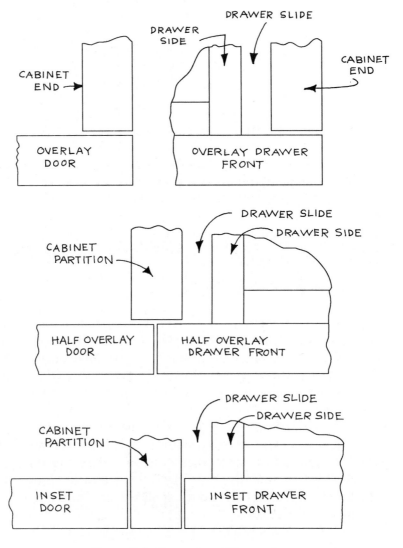

Figure 9-1 Three door-fitting systems

cabinet; half overlay; and inset, or flush. Inset doors and drawer fronts are more often used on furniture than cabinets. In this case the door or drawer front is set inside the cabinet opening. The three fitting systems are shown in Figure 9-1.

Full overlay doors and drawer fronts are usually used on the ends of cabinets. Half-overlay doors and drawer fronts are used when the door or drawer is mounted on an interior partition. Drawer fronts may extend beyond the drawer box enough to form a full overlay on one side and only enough to form a half overlay on the other side.

PULLS AND THEIR INSTALLATION

Any of the drawer and door pulls described in Chapter 4 may be used. If the wood continuous pull is used, the door or drawer front must be cut shorter by the width of the pull material so that when it is installed, the drawer will be at the specified height.

To install the wood continuous pull, a groove must be cut in the top edge of the drawer front or door to fit the tongue on the pull. The groove is usually cut before the door or drawer front is edge-banded to prevent cutting through the edge banding.

The tongue on the continuous pull must be cut back at either end so it won't show on the door or drawer-front edges. Figures 9-2 and 9-3 show this

Figure 9-2 Using a jointer to notch the tongue on the left end of a piece of continuous pull

Figure 9-3 Using a jointer to notch the tongue on the right end of a piece of continuous pull

being done on a jointer. Note that the right-hand end is cut at the far right of the cutter head so that the small lip on the pull material is not cut away. The left-hand end of the pull is cut at the left end of the jointer cutter head for the same reason.

The pulls are then glued and clamped to the door or drawer front using care not to cock the pull in relation to the door or drawer front. This pull is normally installed on doors *after* the hinge holes have been bored because the pull is thicker than the door and would not allow the door to lay flat on the boring table. Machining for joining drawer sides directly to drawer fronts should also be done before attaching the pull, for the same reason.

DOORS

After doors have been edge-banded, they are bored for hinges, and the hinges are installed as described in Chapter 7. The location of the 35-mm hinge cup hole must be determined, both from the top and bottom of the door as well as from the edge.

The distance from the edge of the door is known as the drilling distance and usually varies between 3 mm and 6 mm. The actual drilling distance depends upon the amount of door overlay desired and the thickness of the door. This distance will also vary between hinge manufacturers because of different hinge geometry, and even between different hinge models from the same manufacturer. Each hinge manufacturer can furnish data that should be followed.

Hinge spacing from the top and bottom of the door (usually 2 to 4 in.) will depend on the system hole spacing in the cabinet. If the system holes are in 32-mm multiples, starting from the center of the top cabinet stretcher, then the spacing from the top of the door to the center of the top hinge will also be a multiple of 32 mm. This also assumes that, if there is a drawer above the door, its

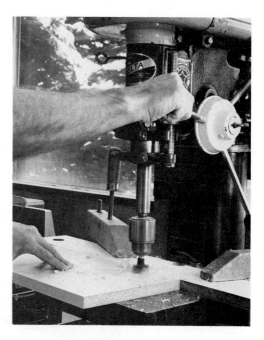

Figure 9-4 Using a drill press to bore hinge holes in door

height is also a multiple of 32 mm. If the total cabinet height is not a multiple of 32 mm, the bottom hinge will be located in multiples of 32 mm from the top hinge rather than from the bottom of the cabinet door. If a continuous pull is to be used on the door, the hinge holes are bored before the pull is installed, so an allowance for the height of the pull must be made when measuring for hinge placement.

Once the hinge location has been determined, the door can be bored and the hinges installed in the door. This may be done using a drill press and a 35-mm bit (Figure 9-4), a special drill-press attachment (Figure 9-5), one of the minipresses marketed by the hinge manufacturers (Figure 9-6), or one of the larger hinge-boring and -inserting machines.

If a drill press and 35-mm bit are the only means of installing hinges, then screw-on hinges (without plastic mounting dowels) must be used. After the hole is drilled, the hinge is tapped into the hole, aligned, and screwed directly to the door. If a drill-press attachment, a minipress, or a larger hinge-boring

Figure 9-5 A drill-press attachment for boring doors for a press-in type of hinge. (Courtesy of Mepla, Inc., Furniture Fittings)

Figure 9-7 Pressing a hinge into a door

and -inserting machine is used, they will drill the two 8-mm holes for the plastic dowels at the same time that the 35-mm hinge cup hole is being drilled. The hinges are then pressed into the door, as shown in Figure 9-7.

The minipresses and larger presses have adjustable stops for locating the hinge holes from the top and bottom of the door.

INSTALLING THE DOOR

The hinge-mounting plates are usually installed in the cabinet system holes before the cabinet is assembled. In the event that system holes are not being used to mount door hinge plates, a simple jig such as the one shown in Figure 9-8 can be used to locate the hinge-mounting-plate screw holes. A horizontal line at hinge center height is drawn from the front edge of the cabinet where each hinge is to go. The jig is indexed against the front edge of the cabinet with the "V" notch on the horizontal line. The two holes can then be used to mark screw locations for the hinge-mounting plates. The marks can then be punched and drilled for screws. In this case, mounting plates with small holes for wood screws will probably be used, rather than ones with larger holes for Euroscrews.

To mount the door on the cabinet, the hinges are opened on the door and guided onto the mounting-plate track. When both hinges are engaged,

Figure 9-8 Jig for locating hinge plate mounting holes when system holes are not used

the clamping screw on each hinge is tightened. The door is closed, and the gap between the back of the door and the face of the cabinet is checked. This is usually about 1 mm. If the gap is too large, small, or uneven, the clamping screw may be loosened and the door moved in or out in relation to the face of the cabinet. When this gap is correct, the door can be adjusted up or down, if necessary, by loosening the height-adjusting screws. Finally, the door may be adjusted from side to side so that it is in vertical alignment with the cabinet. The sideways-adjusting screw will move the door left or right, depending on which way the screw is turned. If the doors are hung in the shop, the final adjustment will be made after the cabinets are installed at the job site.

There are special hinges available for 45°-angle corner cabinets, for zero protrusion to allow clearance for roll-out shelves, for blind-corner applications, for thick doors, and for glass doors. These are described in Chapter 4.

DRAWERS

Drawers may be either built as a box with a drawer front attached later, or built with the drawer sides and bottom attached directly to the drawer front, making the drawer front an integral part of the drawer.

The first method uses an extra piece of material and results in a thicker drawer front, but is faster for most shops and makes it easier to align drawer fronts with doors and other cabinet components.

The components for the drawer box are usually made of 12-mm or 1/2-in.-thick material. They may be joined with dovetails, dowels, wafer plates, or dado-rabbet. The drawer bottom is usually made of 1/4-in. material and may be stapled directly to the bottom of the drawer box if bottom-mounting drawer runners are used. Otherwise, the drawer bottom should be supported in a groove in the drawer sides, front and back.

Drawer fronts can be screwed directly to the drawer or one of the drawer-front adjuster systems available from the hardware manufacturers may be used.

If the drawer front is to be an integral part of the drawer, the material and jointing-system options are the same except that the drawer sides are sometimes attached to the drawer front with dovetail dados, as shown in Figure 9-9.

Another way of making drawers is to purchase the metal drawer sides with built-in runners from one of the hardware manufacturers. The cabinet shop supplies the back, bottom, and drawer front.

Most of the bottom- and side-mount drawer-runner systems require 12.5-mm or 1/2-in. clearance on both sides of the drawer, although some of the full-extension guides require more clearance. There are also runners

Figure 9-9 Using a dovetail dado to attach a drawer front to a drawer side

designed to be mounted in a groove in the drawer side to reduce the required side clearance.

The cabinet-mounted member of the drawer-runner system is usually mounted on the cabinet sides or partions using the system holes, before the cabinet is assembled. If system holes are not being used to mount the drawer runners, a runner-mounting tool may be purchased from the hardware manufacturer to hold the drawer runner in place inside the cabinet while drilling screw holes (Figure 9-10).

Several equipment and hardware manufacturers market machines specifically for boring dowel holes in drawer components, allowing very rapid drawer assembly. Some of these are shown in Figures 9-11 and 9-12.

Figure 9-10 Jig for holding drawer runners in place for mounting when system holes are not used. (Courtesy of Julius Blum, Inc.)

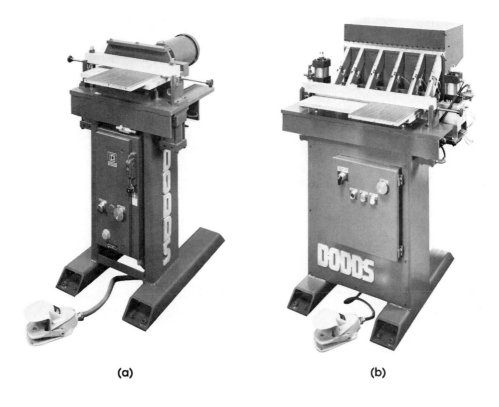

(a)

(b)

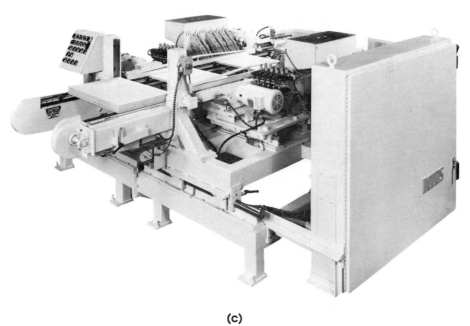

(c)

Figure 9-11 Automatic dowel-boring and -inserting machines for production drawer making. (Courtesy of Alexander Dodds Company)

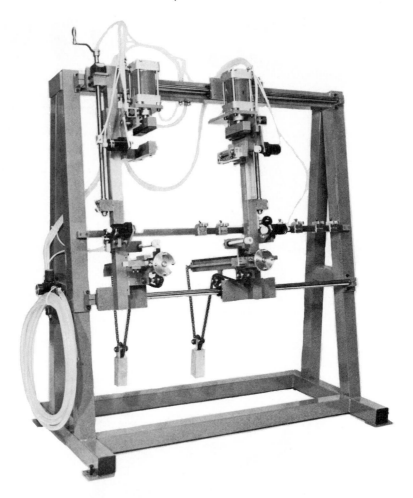

Figure 9-12 Another production drawer-making system. (Courtesy of Mepla, Inc., Furniture Fittings)

FITTING DRAWERS

Some of the drawer runners have elongated screw holes for some of the mounting screws so that final adjustments can be made to get the proper clearance between drawers, doors, and other components. However, some do not, so it is important that screw holes be located accurately. Adjustable drawer fronts help in this regard.

Bottom-mount runners usually have a side-to-side adjustment. Side-mount runners may have to be shimmed if it is necessary to move the drawer left or right.

Drawer-height clearance must be achieved by making the drawer front slightly shorter in height than its nominal dimension. For example, if drawers are to be 128 mm high, they should be made slightly shorter (126 mm) to provide clearance between drawers.

SECTION THREE

Construction
of Face-Frame Cabinets

Traditional face-frame cabinets remain popular with many customers. The construction of face-frame cabinets tends to be quite labor intensive, so it is important to develop efficient construction methods.

Section three includes Chapters 10 to 14 and presents well-proven techniques for building face-frame cabinets. Chapter 10 covers the construction of the face frame, which is potentially one of the most labor intensive operations. Chapter 11 presents many options for making frame-and-panel doors as well as flat doors, sliding doors, and tambour doors. Chapter 12 covers drawer design and construction as well as guide systems. Chapter 13 discusses cabinet cut out and machining, and Chapter 14 covers cabinet assembly.

CHAPTER 10

Machining and Assembling the Face Frame

The face frame is often made and assembled before the cabinet is built because it takes less room to store an assembled face frame than it does an assembled cabinet. In fact, it is best if the face frame, drawers, and doors are all built before the cabinet body is assembled. This allows the face frame, doors, and drawers to be fitted to the cabinet before it is moved from the assembly bench. If these parts are not ready for installation when the cabinet body is assembled, it must be moved to a storage area, then brought back for final assembly.

The joinery used to assemble the face-frame parts is important. There are heavy loads involved, especially when self-closing hinges are used for the doors. The most popular joints used for joining face-frame members are the mortise-and-tenon joint, the butt joint with dowels, and the butt joint with screws, as shown in Figures 3-4 through 3-6. The mortise-and-tenon joint is the strongest and is used in most of the examples in this chapter.

For cabinets built for commercial use, and even for some residential cabinets, the architect may specify one of three levels of construction quality as specified by the Architectural Woodwork Institute.* This may determine the type of joint used.

*"Architectural Woodwork Quality Standards and Guide Specifications" (Arlington, Va.: Architectural Woodwork Institute, 1988).

SIZING ROUGH LUMBER

Face-frame parts and other solid wood parts are often cut from rough-sawn hardwood lumber. When this is the case, the lumber must be straightened and planed to a uniform thickness before the face frame or other parts are cut to size. Rough-sawn lumber is often warped, so it is important that the cabinet-maker understands the process for truing up warped lumber.

The first step in truing warped lumber is to joint one face on the jointer (Figure 10-1). It is important that the board not be allowed to rock while being face-jointed. This will cause the jointed surface to have a twist or bow. The board must be held flat as it passes over the knives so that the high spots are planed off and the board will lie flat.

A push block such as the one shown in Figure 10-1 should be used when face-jointing lumber, and a fairly light cut should be taken.

After the board has been jointed on one face, the opposite face is planed parallel with the first, using a thickness planer (Figure 10-2).

Figure 10-1 Face-jointing a warped board. Note the push block used when face-jointing lumber

Figure 10-2 Using the thickness planer to plane lumber to final thickness

When these two operations have been properly completed, the board will be flat and uniform in thickness. The board may now be planed down to its final desired thickness. If a number of boards are to be planed to the same thickness, they should all be face-jointed first and then all planed to thickness as a group so that the final sizing is done at one machine setting. This ensures that all boards are a uniform thickness, which will facilitate later joining operations.

It should be noted that the thickness planer and the jointer serve different purposes in truing and surfacing rough stock. The thickness planer alone will not straighten twisted or crooked boards. It will merely plane the top surface of a board (on single-head models) parallel to the bottom surface. If a rough, twisted board is planed, the finished result will be a smooth, twisted board! The jointer, on the other hand, will establish a flat surface on one face of the board by planing the high spots flat. However, if the board is then turned over and the second face is planed on the jointer, there is no assurance that it will be parallel to the first face. Therefore, both machines are needed to true warped lumber. If a wide jointer and thickness planer are not available, presurfaced lumber should be purchased.

After the boards have been trued and planed to thickness, the next step is to establish a straight edge on each board. This is also done on the jointer (Figure 10-3).

Figure 10-3 Edge-jointing a board

CUTTING FACE-FRAME PARTS

We are now ready to rip the boards into stock face-frame widths, using the table saw. The widths of typical face-frame components are 2 1/2 in., 2 in., 1 1/2 in., and 1 in., so we should cut sufficient material in each of these widths to make the required number of parts. When ripping boards to width, the widest parts on the list should be cut first, then the next widest, and so forth. The narrow parts can often be cut from the waste material that remains after making the wide cuts. Figure 10-4 shows the face-frame parts being cut to width.

There is one other important consideration in cutting face-frame material. Any edge of a face-frame member that is visible on the finished cabinet should have a planed edge rather than a sawn edge. For example, the left stile on the finished end of the cabinet will show on both edges, so both edges must be planed. The 2 1/2-in. top rail, however, will be covered by the countertop on the top edge, and the bottom edge is hidden by drawers, so it may have

Figure 10-4 Ripping the face-frame material to standard widths. Notice the push stick used for cutting narrow boards on the table saw. (The saw guard has been removed for clarity in showing the operation.)

sawn edges. The pieces that require planed edges must be cut slightly oversize (1/32 to 1/16 in.) to allow for planing to final width on the jointer (Figure 10-5).

The table saw, if used improperly, can be a potentially dangerous machine. The operator should be thoroughly familiar with its operation before attempting to use it. In addition to the general safety rules that apply when operating other machines, the following rules should be observed:

1. The height of the saw blade should be adjusted so that it protrudes only 1/8 to 1/4 in. above the surface of the material being cut.
2. A push stick such as the one shown in Figure 10-4 should be used for pushing narrow boards between the saw blade and the rip fence. Note that the board remaining between the fence and the blade must be pushed past the rear of the blade before being released.
3. One should never attempt to make freehand cuts on the table saw. The slightest twisting will cause the board to bind on the saw blade and be thrown back at the operator. The rip fence must be used when ripping long boards to width, and the sliding miter gauge, as shown in Figure 10-6, must be used when crosscutting boards to length. Boards to be ripped against the rip fence must have a straight edge

Figure 10-5 Edge-planing a
face-frame part to final width
to remove saw marks

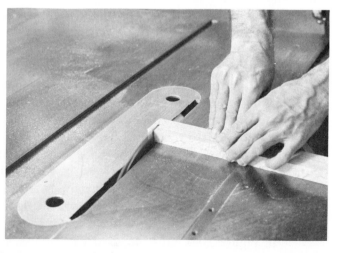

Figure 10-6 Using the table-saw miter gauge for crosscutting

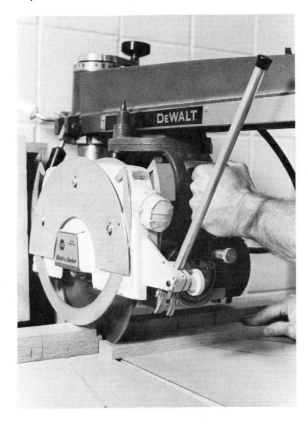

Figure 10-7 Cutting the face-frame parts to length on the radial-arm saw

against the fence and a flat face to lay on the table to prevent possible binding. The miter gauge and rip fence are not to be used at the same time.

After pieces are cut to standard widths, they are cut to the lengths as listed on the cutting list, using the radial-arm saw (Figure 10-7).

The rough ends should be trimmed and checked for any splits before the finished lengths are cut.

LAYOUT FOR MACHINING

Once the parts are cut to finish sizes, the location of the mortise-and-tenon or other joints must be marked on the parts. Before the layout process begins, each part should be examined to determine the better face to be exposed. The back surface of each board is then marked (Figure 10-8). The reasons for this will become apparent when we begin machining the face frame.

Figure 10-8 The back side of each face-frame part is marked.

The face-frame members are then set on a bench in the positions they will occupy on the finished frame (Figure 10-9). The end of each member that is to have a tenon is marked (Figure 10-10). The location of each mortise is also marked.

If dowels are being used rather than mortise-and-tenon joints, the process is similar and the location of the dowel centers is marked.

Figure 10-9 Face-frame parts set in position for layout marking

Figure 10-10   All ends to be tenoned are marked.

MACHINING FACE-FRAME JOINTS

The mortise part of the mortise-and-tenon joint is usually machined first because the thickness of the cut is established by the size of the mortising chisel. The tenon thickness can then be adjusted to fit.

The mortises are cut on a hollow chisel mortiser such as the one shown in Figures 10-11 and 10-12. If the tenons are to be 1 in. long, for example, the mortises should be at least 1 1/8 in. deep to allow space for excess glue and wood chips.

The face of each board should be placed against the guide fence on the mortiser. The mark that you made on the back side of the board will be visible on the outside (Figure 10-13). This is very important. If the mortise is not located in the exact center of the board, it will not matter as long as all boards are machined with the face side against the fence. However, if some of the boards are machined with the back side against the fence and the mortise is not centered, the face surfaces of the joint will be offset, as shown in Figure 10-14. The same is true when locating dowel holes. The mortises are now machined at all locations as marked.

If the mortise occurs at the end of a board—as it would at the top of a stile where it accepts the top rail, for example—the mortise should not be machined to full depth all the way to the end of the board, as this would make it easy to split the board. Instead, the mortise and tenon are haunched, as shown in Figure 10-15.

The tenons may be machined in a number of ways. Single-end tenon machines, as shown in Figure 10-16, work very well but often are not available

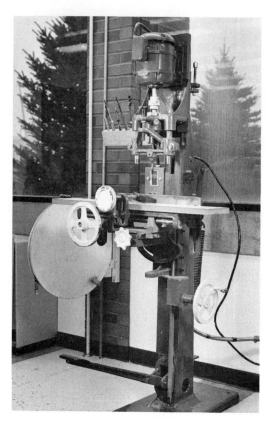

Figure 10-11 Hollow chisel mortiser

in the smaller shop. Tenons may also be easily and accurately machined on a table saw with a good dado set. Figure 10-17 shows a tenon being cut on a table saw.

Notice that the miter gauge is used to push the stock through the cutter and the rip fence is used as a guide to ensure that both shoulder cuts are exactly equal. Normally, the rip fence and miter gauge are not used together, but in this case no piece is being cut off that could become trapped between the blade and fence and be thrown from the machine. The depth of the dado cut establishes the thickness of the tenon. The tenons on the top rails must then be haunched, as shown in Figure 10-18.

Figure 10-19 shows the machined parts of a face frame ready for assembly.

If a pull board (breadboard) is specified for a cabinet, its opening should be cut in the top face-frame rail before the face frame is assembled. If the pull board is 3/4 in. thick, the face-frame opening is 13/16 in. wide. The top of the opening is usually 1 in. from the top of the rail.

The horizontal (long) cuts for the pull board may be carefully made on the table saw using the following procedure:

Figure 10-12 Machining the mortise

Figure 10-13 Mounting the board in the mortiser with face to fence (mark out)

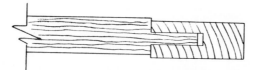

Figure 10-14 Mortise-and-tenon joint not properly centered

Figure 10-15 Haunched mortise and tenon

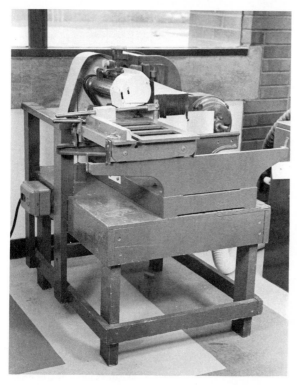

Figure 10-16 Single-end tenoner

Figure 10-17 Machining a tenon using a table saw with a dado set

1. Draw the location of the pull-board cutout on the face-frame rail. Extend the end lines all the way across the rail, as shown in Figure 10-20.
2. Set the table-saw blade at a height that will allow the blade to extend through the face-frame rail by about 1/4 in. Mark the location of the

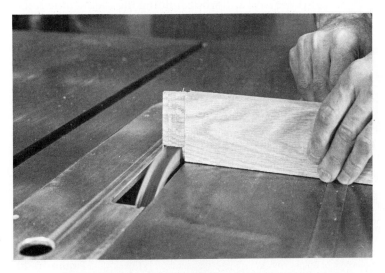

Figure 10-18 Haunching tenons on the top rail

Figure 10-19 Machined face-frame parts ready for assembly

back and front positions of the blade on the rip fence, as shown in Figure 10-21.

3. Crank the blade below the table, counting the number of turns of the handle required to lower the blade below the table.

4. Set the rip fence 1 in. away from the blade for the first cut. Position the face-frame rail so that the line representing one end of the opening is in line with the back line drawn on the rip fence (Figure 10-22).

5. Clamp a feather board to the rip fence, as shown in Figure 10-23. This will keep the stock from raising off the table when the blade is raised into the wood.

6. Start the saw, and while holding the face-frame rail with the left hand,

Figure 10-20 Layout for pull-board cutout

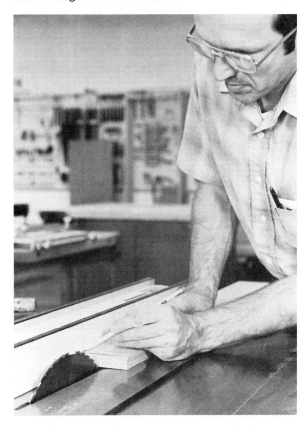

Figure 10-21 Marking the front and rear of the blade on the rip fence

Figure 10-22 Aligning the mark on the face frame with the rear mark on the rip fence

Figure 10-23 Clamping a feather board to the rip fence

crank the blade up through the rail to its previous height (counting the turns). Then run the face-frame rail until the mark on the other end of the cutout lines up with the front mark on the rip fence (Figure 10-24).

7. The other horizontal cut is made in the same manner. The end cuts are then made with a saber saw (Figure 10-25).

Figure 10-24 Finishing the cut

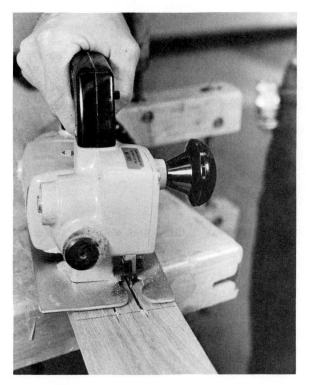

Figure 10-25 Making the end cuts with a saber saw

FACE-FRAME ASSEMBLY

The face-frame parts are glued, clamped, and checked for squareness before being attached to the cabinet. It is a good practice to dry-fit the parts of the first face frame on a job to make sure that all parts fit properly before glue is applied.

If the face frame is assembled face down in the clamps, glue may be applied to the face side of the mortise and the back side of the tenon, as shown in Figure 10-26. This will prevent glue from being squeezed out the face side of the joint. Having the face down while clamping leaves the back of the face frame exposed; the tenon may be pinned with short staples from the back so that it may be removed from the clamps immediately (Figure 10-27).

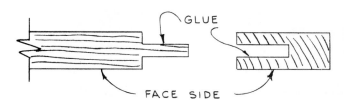

Figure 10-26 Mortise-and-tenon joint showing proper glue replacement. Excess glue will not be forced from the face of the joint with this method.

Figure 10-27 Stapling the back side of the mortise-and-tenon joint

Before the joint is pinned, however, the face frame should be checked for squareness by measuring diagonally from corner to corner (Figure 10-28). Any out of squareness can be easily corrected at this stage by angling the clamps in the direction of the longer diagonal measurement (Figure 10-29).

If a wide-belt sander is available, the face frame may receive a preliminary sanding before being mounted on the cabinet (Figure 10-30). At this point, the face frame is set aside until the cabinet body is assembled.

Figure 10-28 Checking the face frame for squareness

Figure 10-29   Placing the clamps at an angle to pull the face frame square

Figure 10-30   Sanding the assembled face frame with a wide-belt sander

CHAPTER 11

Doors for Face-Frame Cabinets

First impressions are important! Most people get their first impression of a set of cabinets from the doors. The doors usually constitute the majority of the visible surface of a set of cabinets, and their styling determines the style of the cabinets. If the exterior surfaces such as doors and drawer fronts are not attractive, very few potential customers will look beyond the surface to see the excellent-quality workmanship and convenience features that you may have built into the cabinets. In remodel work, many otherwise functional cabinets are replaced with new cabinets simply because the homeowner wants to improve the appearance of the house. The cabinetmaker should always consider the appearance of doors and drawer fronts.

Of course, doors also serve functional purposes. They conceal the contents of the cabinet and keep out dust. They may also be equipped with locks to secure the contents of the cabinet. They may have racks, trays, or shelves mounted on their inside surface for additional storage.

In this chapter we discuss the three types of hinged doors and some of the more popular styles of cabinet doors. We then present the construction techniques and procedures for making these doors. We also discuss two nonhinged doors: sliding bypass doors and tambour doors. The procedure for installing doors is covered in Chapter 14.

TYPES OF DOORS

Cabinet doors are often classified according to how they are mounted on the cabinet. The three basic types are lip doors, overlay doors, and flush doors.

The lip door has a rabbet (usually 3/8-in. by 3/8-in.) along the door edges. The lip resulting from the rabbet laps over the face-frame member, as shown in Figure 11-1.

This lip-type door is relatively easy to fit because the lip does not leave a visible gap between the door and the face frame. Figure 11-2 shows a cabinet with a lip-type door.

Overlay doors (Figures 11-3 through 11-5 are mounted on the face-frame surface and cover the door opening. They are sometimes made with a beveled edge that provides a gripping surface for opening the door, thus eliminating the need for door pulls. Overlay doors are also used on cabinets without face frames, as shown in Figure 11-5.

Flush doors are set in the face-frame opening so that the outside surface of the door is flush with the face of the cabinet (Figure 11-6). These doors are much more difficult to fit than the lip or overlay doors because the gap between the door and the face frame is visible. This means that the door must

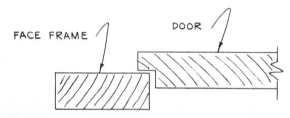

Figure 11-1 Lip door

Figure 11-2 Cabinet with lip door

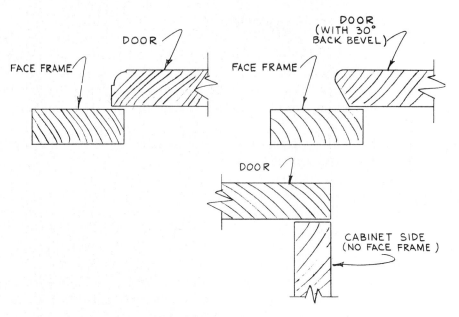

Figure 11-3 Overlay doors

Figure 11-4 Cabinet with overlay doors

Figure 11-5 Cabinets with overlay doors without face frames

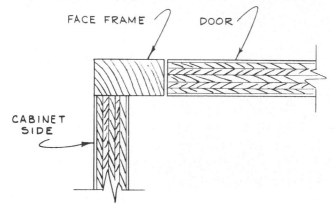

Figure 11-6 Flush door

be very accurately fitted within the opening so that the edge gap is uniform. This gap should be about the thickness of a dime. Occasionally, the settling that often occurs in a new house will cause a noticeable difference in the fit of flush doors from the way they were fitted when installed.

DOOR STYLES

The simplest cabinet door to make is a flat door. While such doors are not as stylish as some, they are preferred by many people for their "clean," unadorned lines and for ease of cleaning. They are usually made of veneer-core or, occasionally, lumber-core plywood. Flat doors are rarely made from laminated solid lumber because of its tendency to warp. Figure 11-7 shows a

Figure 11-7 Cabinet with flat doors

cabinet with flat doors. Notice that the grain is matched between drawer fronts and between door and drawer fronts.

Frame-and-panel doors are very popular for cabinets and furniture. They consist of a frame made up of two stiles, two rails, and a panel (Figure 11-8).

With frame-and-panel construction, an almost unlimited number of door styles may be developed. The door frame may be molded to various shapes on the inside edge, outside edge, or both edges. The panel may be flat, flat with V grooves, raised, or carved. The top and bottom rails may be arched or straight. The panel may be made of something other than wood, such as glass, plastic, caning, or expanded metal mesh. Figure 11-9 shows several of the more popular frame-and-panel doors.

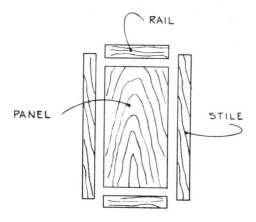

Figure 11-8 Frame-and-panel door components

(a)

(b)

(c)

(d)

Figure 11-9 Frame-and-panel doors

185

Figure 11-10 "European" door

Another type of door showing a European influence is the flat door with tongue-and-groove boards, shown in Figure 11-10. This is in reality a frame-and-panel door whose panel is made of a number of tongue-and-groove-fitted boards.

MAKING FLAT DOORS

Flat doors are usually made from 3/4-in. hardwood plywood to match the cabinet. They are cut to cover the cabinet opening plus a certain amount of the cabinet face frame. Lip doors cover the cabinet face frame 1/4 in. on each lip. Such a door would therefore be cut 1/2 in. wider than the opening to allow for the lip (see the cutting list in Figure 11-11). Note that the door extends over the face frame only 1/4 in. even though the lip on the door is 3/8 in. This leaves 1/8-in. clearance, or a total of 1/4 in. for a door with lips on both edges. The hinges use part of this clearance. The clearance that remains allows some latitude in lining up the doors on the cabinet face.

The drawer fronts are usually cut at the same time as the doors so that they can be grain-matched. Figure 11-11 shows a cabinet drawing and a cutting list for its doors and drawer fronts. Note that the cutting list calls for one large

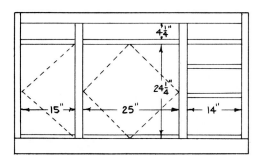

DOOR & DRAWER FRONTS:

1 Pc $\frac{3}{4}$ × 15$\frac{1}{2}$ × 30 (LEFT DOOR & DWR.)
1 Pc $\frac{3}{4}$ × 25$\frac{1}{2}$ × 30 (CENTER)
1 Pc $\frac{3}{4}$ × 14$\frac{1}{2}$ × 30 (RIGHT DWR. FRONTS)

Figure 11-11   Cutting list for plywood lip-type doors and drawer fronts

piece to make up the drawer fronts for the bank of drawers. This will later be cut into individual drawer fronts and the pieces kept in sequence so that the grain will match on all the fronts.

After developing the cutting list, it is sometimes helpful to lay out a plywood cutting plan on a sheet of paper. This consists of sketching a sheet of plywood to scale, usually 1 in. = 1 ft., and then drawing the cuts on the paper. This is an aid to obtaining the best possible cuttings from the sheet. The cuts should not be drawn directly on the plywood sheet.

The plywood parts are then cut to size on the table saw. When cutting plywood, a very fine tooth blade made especially for plywood should be used to avoid chipping the face veneers and to provide a smooth cut for the exposed edges. Figure 11-12 shows a carbide-tipped plywood blade and a steel plywood blade. Some table saws are equipped with a small scoring blade ahead of the main cutting blade to eliminate chipping on the underside of the cut.

Figure 11-13 shows the technique to use when making the first cut across the sheet. Note the support rail on the left side of the table saw and the table behind the saw used to support the plywood sheet.

Figure 11-12   Carbide-tipped and steel plywood blades

Figure 11-13-a Starting the plywood crosscut. (The saw guard has been removed for clarity in showing the operation.)

Figure 11-13-b Finishing the plywood crosscut

Figure 11-14 shows the technique for cutting a sheet of plywood lengthwise. It is usually advantageous to make cuts across the sheet before making cuts the length of the sheet. If the long narrow pieces are cut first, they are difficult to crosscut safely and accurately on the table saw unless the saw is equipped with a sliding table.

After the doors are cut to finished size, they are then "lipped" by cutting a 3/8-in. by 3/8-in. rabbet on all sides that lip over the face frame. Doors that are in pairs (two doors for one opening) are usually cut in one piece, lipped, and then cut into two doors to avoid accidentally lipping the edge where the two doors join.

There are a number of ways of lipping doors, and the technique used may depend upon the type of equipment available. A table saw may be used with a dado head, as shown in Figure 11-15.

A spindle shaper is probably the most common machine used for lipping doors. A good, sharp carbide cutter is necessary to avoid chipping the face veneer on the plywood (Figure 11-16).

A router mounted on a router table may also be used, as shown in Figure 11-17. Again the cutter must be very sharp and should be carbide-tipped. A steel cutter will dull in the area where it is cutting the plywood glue line after just a few cuts.

Figure 11-14 Cutting a plywood sheet lengthwise

Figure 11-15 Lipping plywood doors with a dado head on a table saw

Figure 11-16 Lipping doors with a spindle shaper

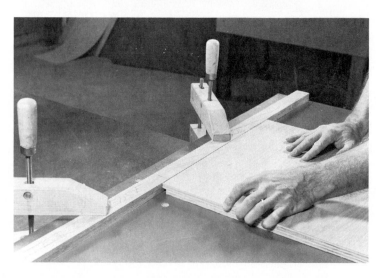

Figure 11-17 Lipping doors with a table-mounted portable router

MAKING FRAME-AND-PANEL DOORS

The frame for a frame-and-panel door is very similar in construction to the face frame discussed in Chapter 10. The stiles and rails may be joined with either mortise-and-tenon joints or with dowels. A simple frame-and-panel door would consist of a frame with a groove around the inside for a 1/4-in. plywood panel. Figure 11-18 shows some typical frame-and-panel shapes used for cabinet doors.

The molded edge shown on the inside edge of the frame members in Figure 11-18 is known as sticking. A number of different sticking shapes may be used to change the appearance of the doors. But such sticking does present a problem in joining the stiles and rails. If the door frame has no molding or sticking, as in Figure 11-18a the door rails may be joined to the stiles with a simple mortise-and-tenon joint or a butt joint with dowels. However, if the stiles have sticking, the rails must be cope-cut to match the sticking (Figure 11-19).

This system of joining door stiles and rails is almost universally used by large production cabinet shops and furniture manufacturers, whose production molding machines and double-end tenoners are set up to make the mating cuts. This joint can be made in the smaller shop using a spindle shaper and a matched set of cutters. Figure 11-20 shows a shaper built specifically for making doors in which both cutters are mounted on the same shaft. The cabinetmaker runs the stiles and rails through one set of knives to produce

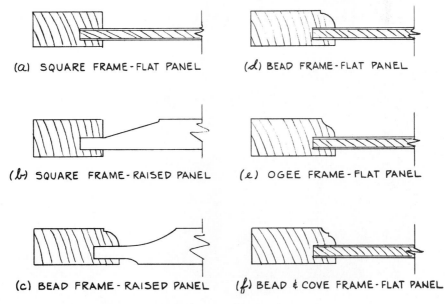

(a) SQUARE FRAME - FLAT PANEL

(d) BEAD FRAME - FLAT PANEL

(b) SQUARE FRAME - RAISED PANEL

(e) OGEE FRAME - FLAT PANEL

(c) BEAD FRAME - RAISED PANEL

(f) BEAD & COVE FRAME - FLAT PANEL

Figure 11-18 Typical frame-and-panel details

Figure 11-19 Cope cut on end of rail to match sticking on the stile

Figure 11-20 Special shaper for making cabinet doors. (Courtesy of the Hammer Machinery Co., Inc., Santa Rosa, California)

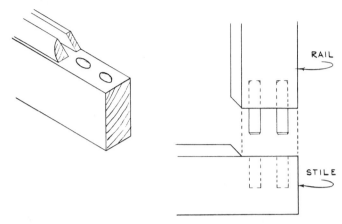

Figure 11-21 Sticking cut away from the stile and mitered to fit the rail sticking

the edge sticking and then runs the ends of the rails through the other set to produce the matching cope cut. Notice that the machine has three worktables to utilize three sets of knives on the single spindle.

Several other methods of making stile and rail doors are available to the cabinetmaker who does not want to invest in the matched cutters or who does not have access to a shaper. One technique is to carefully cut the sticking away where the rail joins the stile, leaving a flat surface for a butt joint with dowels (Figure 11-21). Obviously, great care must be exercised in cutting the miter on the sticking. The finished appearance of the face of the door will be the same with this method as with the previously described method of coping the joint.

Another alternative is to assemble the stiles and rails with a miter joint (Figure 11-22). This method neatly eliminates the necessity of coping the joint,

Figure 11-22 Stile and rail assembled with a miter joint

Figure 11-23 Sticking machined by a router after the frame has been assembled. Notice that the sticking is round in the corner.

but it is not without its difficulties. The assembly of a miter joint is more difficult than a butt joint or mortise-and-tenon joint because the joint must be clamped across the width of the door and along its length. The clamps must be uniformly tightened to avoid having the miters "creep."

Another alternative is to assemble the frame and glue a flat panel to the back of it. The sticking is then machined by running a router with a suitable molding cutter around the inside of the frame. The disadvantage of this method is that the panel must be applied to the back of the frame, and some people also object to the rounded corner detail produced by the router, as shown in Figure 11-23.

Yet another method is to make the door frame square (without sticking) and attach a quarter-round or other molding after the door is assembled. These moldings are mitered at the corners and give the appearance of having sticking on the door stiles and rails (Figure 11-24).

Certain styles of doors call for an arched or cathedral top, as shown in Figure 11-25. This is easily accomplished when the sticking is machined with a router as previously described. The top rail is band-sawn to the desired contour, and the pilot bearing on the router is used to follow the contour. When the sticking is machined on the individual stiles and rails with a shaper, depth collars must be used on the spindle to allow the cutter to follow the contour (Figure 11-26).

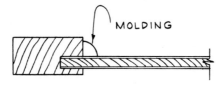

Figure 11-24 Molding applied after the door has been assembled

Figure 11-25 Cathedral-top door

Figure 11-26 Cathedral-top rail being machined on the shaper

Figure 11-27-a Raised panel with straight bevel

Figure 11-27-b Raised panel with cove

Fortunately, the door panel is less complex than the door frame. If the panel is to be flat (1/4-in. plywood, glass, plastic, etc.), it is simply cut to size. The other popular option is the raised panel, usually made from laminated solid lumber. The shape of the raised panel is usually either a bevel, as shown in Figure 11-27-a, or a cove cut, as shown in Figure 11-27-b. These panels are usually made using a spindle shaper with a raised panel cutter. Figure 11-28 shows a cutter for making the cove-shaped cut.

In the absence of a shaper, a suitable raised panel may be made using the table saw. The blade is tilted 15° (a saw in which the blade tilts away from the fence must be used), and the board is run in a vertical position, as shown in Figures 11-29 and 11-30. The panel is then run horizontally to cut the small bevel, as shown in Figure 11-31. All saw marks must then be sanded from the beveled surfaces.

Figure 11-28 Raised panel shaper cutter

A cove-shaped raised panel can also be made with the table saw and a standard dado blade set. The dado set is installed and a wood fence is clamped diagonally across the saw table and over the center of the dado blade, as shown in Figure 11-32. The angle of the wood fence in relation to the dado blade will determine the radius of the cove curve. Running the fence perpendicular to the blade would give a cove with the same radius as the dado blade. The smaller the angle with the blade, the smaller the radius of the cove. It may be necessary to make a few test cuts to get the desired cove radius and width.

The actual cove cut is made by making a series of very light cuts. The first cut is made by raising the blade just above the table and making a cut. The blade is then raised a little more for each successive cut. The last cut should be a very light cut and the feed speed should be very slow to minimize the saw marks that will have to be sanded smooth. The finished raised panel is shown in Figure 11-33.

Figure 11-29 Cutting the bevel for a raised panel on the table saw

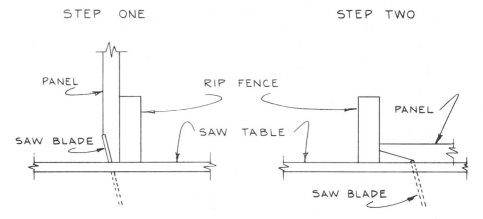

Figure 11-30 The sequence of cuts for making a raised panel on the table saw

The reason for using a dado set for this operation rather than a single-saw blade is that the dado set will leave a flat area at the outside of the cove for inserting the panel into a groove in the door frame (Figure 11-34). A relief cut, as shown in Fig. 11-35, is often made on the back of the panel to help center the panel in the door frame.

Figure 11-31 Cutting the small bevel on the raised panel

Figure 11-32   Setup for cutting a cove-shaped raised panel using a dado head

Figure 11-33   Finished raised panel

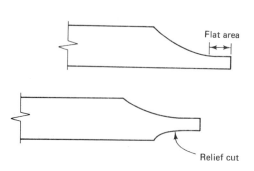

Figure 11-34 Cove cut made with dado head leaves a flat area for inserting panel into grooves in stiles and rails

Flat area

Relief cut

Figure 11-35 Relief cut on back of raised panel

Once the stiles, rails, and panels have been cut and machined, sanding is done to areas that would be difficult to sand after the door is assembled.

You are now ready to assemble the door. After a trial fitting, glue is applied to the adjoining surfaces, taking care not to get glue on exposed surfaces. The door is then clamped across the rails, as shown in Figure 11-36.

As soon as the clamps are tightened, the door must quickly be checked for squareness by measuring diagonally from corner to corner. If the diagonal measurements are not equal, the clamps may be loosened and angled slightly in the direction of the longer diagonal, as shown in Figure 11-37. When they are retightened, the door will be pulled square. In fact, care must be exercised

Figure 11-36 Clamping a frame-and-panel door

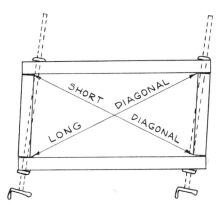

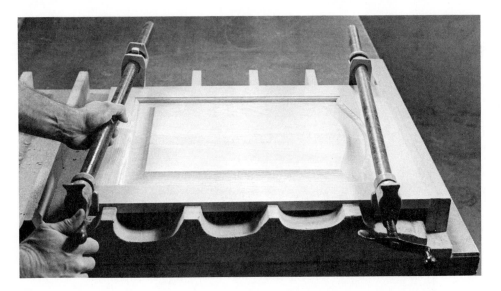

Figure 11-37 Clamps angled to pull the door frame square

not to pull the door out of square in the opposite direction! A pointed stick of appropriate length (Figure 11-38) works well to check diagonal lengths.

In addition to keeping the door square while gluing, it must also be kept flat. Figure 11-39 shows a simple shop-built fixture for squaring doors and keeping them flat.

If any glue is squeezed from the joint while clamping, it should be left to harden and then be cut from the surface with a sharp knife or chisel rather than being wiped while wet. Wiping wet glue, even with a wet cloth, will force it into the pores of the wood and will affect the way the wood accepts a finish.

Making attractive frame-and-panel doors is one of the most difficult operations for a small shop to do economically. One method that is fairly simple consists of making the frame, with square edges. The stiles and rails are

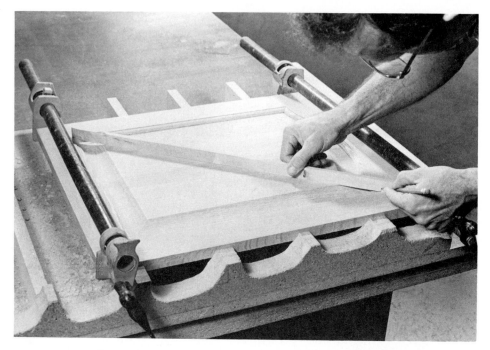

Figure 11-38   Using a stick to check diagonal lengths

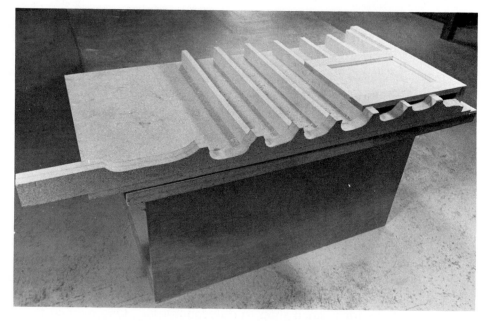

Figure 11-39   Fixture for holding doors square for gluing

Figure 11-40 Clamp nails such as these may be used to assemble a door frame. (Courtesy of Senco Products, Inc.)

doweled or may even be butted and assembled with air-driven clamp nails (Figure 11-40).

A 3/8-in. plywood back is then glued and stapled to the back of the frame. This plywood back is 3/4 in. smaller in width and length than the door frame, leaving a 3/8-in. lip. Finally, the inside edge of the frame is molded with a router. Figure 11-41 shows a section of such a door.

The final step before hanging the doors is to sand the assembled doors. The preliminary sanding may be done on a wide-belt sander when one is available (Figure 11-42). The cross-grain sanding marks will then have to be removed with a finish sander.

The doors may also be sanded with a portable belt sander by first sanding the rails and lightly sanding across the joint (Figure 11-43). The stiles are then sanded, being careful to sand right up to the joint, as shown in Figure 11-44. The final sanding is again done with a finishing sander (Figure 11-45).

Figure 11-41 Frame-and-panel door with the frame mounted on a plywood panel

Figure 11-42 Sanding an assembled door with a wide-belt sander

Figure 11-43 Sanding door rails with a belt sander

Figure 11-44 Sanding the door stiles with a belt sander

Figure 11-45 Final sanding with a finish sander

SLIDING AND TAMBOUR DOORS

Thus far our discussion has dealt only with hinged doors. There are, however, situations where sliding doors are better. They don't require space in front of the cabinet, and when glass doors are required, they eliminate the problems inherent in hinging glass doors. Sliding cabinet doors are usually 1/4-in. plywood, hardboard, glass, or plastic. Figure 11-46 shows a cabinet with sliding doors. Grooved hardwood or plastic track is available and is nailed, stapled, or glued into the cabinet. Occasionally the grooves for the doors may be machined directly into the cabinet top and bottom. The top grooves should be twice as deep as the bottom grooves so that the door can be inserted in the top groove, lifted, and dropped into the bottom groove. Recessed pulls are available for sliding doors.

Another type of sliding door that is sometimes used on cabinets is the tambour door. This door is made from a number of wood slats held together with a canvas backing. This gives it a flexibility that will allow it to slide along a curved track. Its operation is similar to that of a roll-top desk. The track usually runs along the front of the cabinet and then along the side (Figure 11-47). This allows the entire front of the cabinet to be open, as opposed to sliding doors, which allow only one side to be open at a time.

Figure 11-48 shows a cabinet with tambour doors.

Figure 11-46   Cabinet with sliding doors

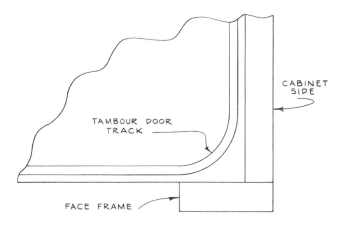

Figure 11-47 Groove cut on cabinet top and bottom for sliding tambour doors

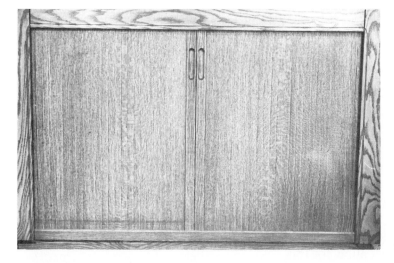

(a)

(b)

Figure 11-48 Cabinet with tambour doors

CHAPTER 12

Drawers for Face-Frame Cabinets

Drawers provide the most efficient storage for many items and should be used whenever possible. However, they do present some construction problems. They must be strong enough to withstand pulling on the drawer front with an item jammed inside the drawer, yet they should not be unduly heavy. They must be accurately fitted so that they slide without an excess of lateral (sideways) motion, yet must not be so tight that they stick. To compound the problem, when the drawer and cabinet are made of wood, they are both subject to shrinking and swelling with changes in humidity, so the drawer-guide system must allow for this.

Some drawers are used for storing heavy objects such as tools or small appliances and must be designed accordingly. In this chapter we look at methods of overcoming these problems.

DRAWER TYPES AND STYLES

Drawers are made to fit the cabinet, using either lip, overlay, or flush construction, just as are the doors (Chapter 11). Their construction usually matches that of the doors. Figure 12-1 shows a plan view of drawers that use each of the three fitting methods.

The style of the drawer front is also designed to match that of the doors, except that frame-and-panel construction is rarely used for drawer fronts.

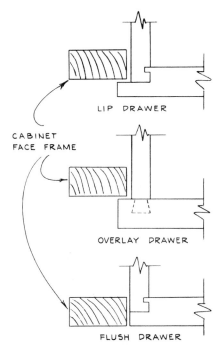

LIP DRAWER

CABINET
FACE FRAME

OVERLAY DRAWER

FLUSH DRAWER

Figure 12-1 Drawer-front fitting methods

When frame-and-panel construction is used on doors, the drawer fronts are made of a matching solid wood and the outside edge is shaped to match that of the door.

When flat plywood is used for the doors, it is also used for the drawer fronts. In this case, the grain is usually run vertically and is matched from one drawer to the next.

DRAWER DESIGN AND CONSTRUCTION

The materials used in drawer construction are usually as follows:

1. *Front:* 3/4-in. hardwood or hardwood plywood
2. *Sides:* 1/2-in. hardwood, softwood, plywood, or medium-density fiberboard
3. *Backs:* 1/2-in. or 3/4-in. hardboard, softwood, plywood, or particle board
4. *Bottom:* 1/4-in. plywood or hardboard

One of the major factors in determining the strength of a drawer is the type of joint selected for joining the sides to the front and back. The joint between the front and sides is especially critical because the force of pulling

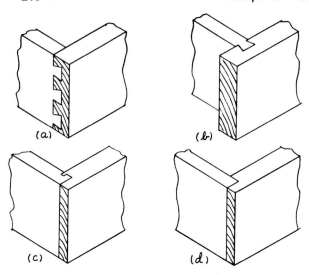

(a)

(b)

(c)

(d)

Figure 12-2 Typical joints used for joining drawer fronts to drawer sides: (a) dovetail, (b) dovetail dado, (c) double dado, (d) rabbet

the drawer open is transferred through this joint. Some of the joints commonly used to assemble drawers are shown in Figure 12-2.

Of the joints shown, the dovetail and dovetail dado are strongest and should be used where heavy loads or hard use is anticipated. The double dado is acceptable for most cabinet construction, and the rabbet is used when lighter loads are anticipated. A butt joint is sometimes used to join the back to the sides in light construction. A dado or rabbet joint may also be used. The drawer bottom is usually set in a groove in the drawer sides and fronts.

MACHINING DRAWER JOINTS

Dovetail joints are made on special dovetail machines in large production shops. In smaller shops they are made using a dovetail cutting accessory for a portable router. The drawer front and mating side are machined together in one operation. Figure 12-3 shows dovetail joints being made this way.

The dovetail dado also uses the portable router. The dovetail groove is cut with a portable router or an overarm router, as shown in Figure 12-4. The dovetail tongue is cut on the table saw by making the shoulder cut first and then making the bevel cuts, as shown in Figure 12-5.

The double dado joint may be made on the table saw. The first step is to make a rabbet on the end of the drawer front, as shown in Figure 12-6.

The second step is to cut out the shaded area shown in Figure 12-6 by running the drawer front over the table saw in a vertical position (Figure 12-7). The final step is to cut a matching dado in the drawer side (Figure 12-8).

There are several drawer-making machines available with matched sets of cutters for machining joints on drawer components. Figure 12-9 shows such

Figure 12-3   Cutting a dovetail joint

Figure 12-4   Cutting a dovetail dado with the overarm router

Figure 12-5-a Making the shoulder cuts for a dovetail using the table saw

Figure 12-5-b Making the dovetail face cut

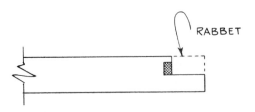

RABBET

Figure 12-6 Rabbet cut for a double dado drawer joint. (The shaded area will be removed next.)

Figure 12-7 Finishing the double dado on the table saw

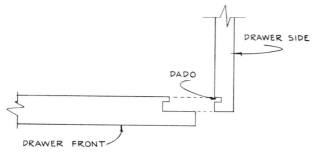

DRAWER SIDE

DADO

DRAWER FRONT

Figure 12-8 Machine work completed for double dado drawer joint

Figure 12-9 Drawer-making machine. (Courtesy of the Hammer Machinery Co., Inc., Santa Rosa, California)

213

a machine for making the double dado joint for assembling drawer fronts, sides, and backs. It also has cutters for lipping doors and drawer fronts, grooving drawer bottoms, and rounding the edges of drawer fronts. Such a machine speeds up the drawer-making process greatly. Figure 12-10 shows a double dado joint being made on this machine.

A final machining operation that is sometimes performed on drawer components is to slightly round or "relieve" the top edge of the drawer sides. This is usually done on a shaper.

In summary, the process for making drawer parts is as follows:

1. Cut all the component parts to exact size. The size of the parts relative to the drawer opening will vary according to the guide system being used. (Guide systems are discussed later in this chapter.)
2. Machine joints for joining drawer front to drawer sides and for joining back to sides.
3. Machine a 3/8-in. lip on drawer front if lip construction is being used.
4. Machine a 1/4-in. groove in the drawer front and sides for the drawer bottom.
5. Relieve the top edge of the drawer sides (optional).
6. Machine any decorative molding desired on the drawer front.
7. Assemble the drawer as described in the following section.

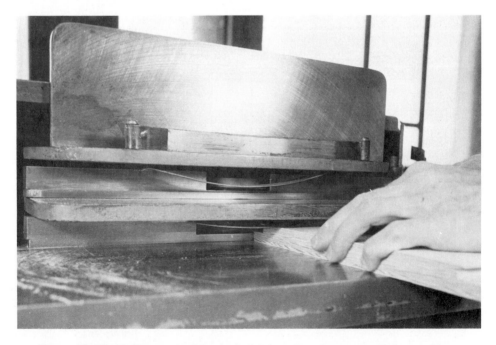

Figure 12-10 Cutting a double dado joint on the drawer-making machine

DRAWER ASSEMBLY

Drawers assembled with dovetail or dovetail dado joints are usually glued and clamped. Care must be taken to keep the drawer flat (avoid twisting) and square while being glued. The diagonal measurements should be checked as described in Chapter 11 for door assembly.

Drawers using the double dado or rabbet joint are usually glued and nailed or stapled together. Figure 12-11 shows a convenient sequence for

Figure 12-11-a Nailing one drawer side to the drawer front

Figure 12-11-b Nailing the second side to the front

Figure 12-11-c Attaching the drawer back

Figure 12-11-d Inserting the drawer bottom

Figure 12-11-e Nailing the drawer bottom to the back

Figure 12-11-f The assembled drawer

assembling such a drawer. Notice the stop block clamped to the bench to keep the drawer parts from sliding while they are being nailed. They may also be assembled with an air nailer or stapler.

DRAWER-GUIDE SYSTEMS

One of the most popular drawer-guide systems used in residential cabinet work is the wood center guide. The basic component of this system is a wood guide rail running from the front to the rear of the cabinet under the center of the drawer, as shown in Figure 12-12. When this system is used, it must be

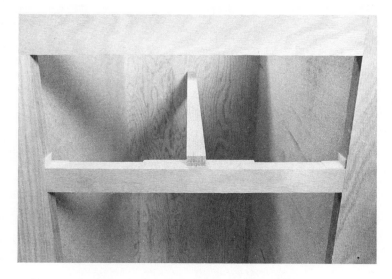

Figure 12-12 Drawer center guide

accompanied by a similar rail above the drawer (Figure 12-13) to keep the drawer from tipping down when pulled more than halfway out. This rail is called a tip rail or kicker. The wood guide is usually used in conjunction with a set of hard nylon guide tabs that locate and guide the drawer along the wood guide rail.

A set of these nylon guides consists of a plastic tab for the left and right side of the drawer opening (Figure 12-14), a U-shaped tab that mounts under the back of the drawer to slide on the bottom rail, and a tab that mounts on the top of the drawer back (Figure 12-15) to slide against the tip rail.

This system requires that the drawer be 1/4 in. less in width and height than the drawer opening (1/8 in. on each side) to allow for the plastic tabs.

The wood center guide is usually made of hardwood and is 3/4 in. thick by 1 3/8 in. wide. The actual width is determined by the width of the front-face frame rail (usually 1 in.) and by the distance of the drawer bottom from the bottom of the drawer side (usually 3/8 in.). The length of the drawer guide is equal to the inside depth of the cabinets plus 3/8 in.

Figure 12-13 Drawer tip rail

Figure 12-14 Plastic guide tabs may be used in the corners of the drawer opening.

The center guide is attached to the cabinet by first cutting a 1-in. by 5/8-in. rabbet across one end and attaching a 1/4-in. by 1-in. by approximately 3-in. plywood tab, as shown in Figure 12-16. This guide is then centered in the drawer opening. The 1/4-in. plywood tab is glued and nailed or stapled from inside the cabinet to the face frame (Figure 12-17).

The back end of the guide is not attached to the cabinet until the drawer is ready to be fitted. After the center guide is attached to the front of the

Figure 12-15 Plastic guide mounted on the drawer bottom. This guide slides on the wood center guide rail shown in Figure 12-12.

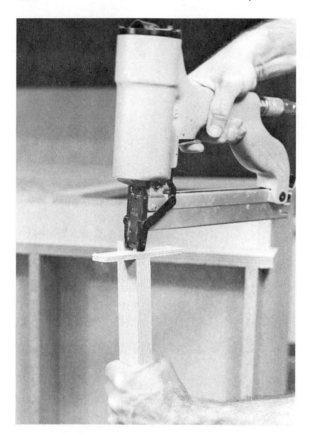

Figure 12-16 Attaching a 1/4-in. plywood tab to a center guide rail before the rail is installed

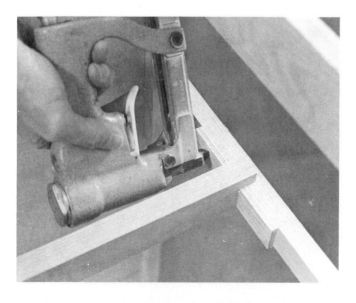

Figure 12-17 The 1/4-in. plywood tab is then glued and stapled to the face-frame rail from inside the cabinet.

cabinet and the plastic tabs are in place, the drawer may be fitted by reaching into the cabinet and supporting the drawer guide with one hand while sliding the drawer into the opening with the other. With the drawer completely closed, the rear of the guide rail may be moved up, down, or sideways to get the best possible fit of the drawer front against the face of the cabinet (Figure 12-18).

Once you have attained a good fit on the drawer, you may staple through the back of the cabinet into the drawer guide with your third hand, or you may have an assistant do it!

Center guide rails are sometimes also used with a hardwood guide, mounted under the drawer, that has a groove that matches the width of the guide rail (Figure 12-19). This would replace the plastic tabs.

Another guide system sometimes used consists of hardwood side guides mounted to the cabinet on either side of the drawer opening and corresponding grooves in the drawer sides (Figure 12-20). This system eliminates the need for a separate tip rail, but it is somewhat more difficult to fit. However, when properly fitted and waxed, it allows the drawer to slide very smoothly.

There are, of course, a number of commercially made roller-guide systems, as described in Chapter 4. These vary a great deal in cost and ease of

Figure 12-18   Fitting a drawer using the center guide system

Figure 12-19 Grooved hardwood guide on the underside of a drawer to match the center guide rail

installation. Center roller guides (Figure 12-21) are fairly inexpensive and are used for low-load applications. Most of the better side-guide systems, such as those shown in Figure 12-22, are very smooth in operation, and some of them are rated at 75 lb. load capacity or higher. These generally require 1/2 in. on

Figure 12-20 Hardwood side guides

Figure 12-21 Center roller guides

Figure 12-22 Side roller guides. (Courtesy of Grass America, Inc., Kernersville, North Carolina)

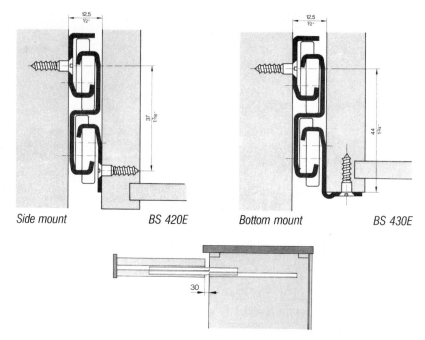

Figure 12-23 A full-extension drawer guide. (Courtesy of Julius Blum, Inc.)

Figure 12-24 Roll-out trays

each side of the drawer (the drawer must be 1 in. narrower than the opening), and they may require extra structural work inside the cabinet to provide a mounting surface flush with the inside edge of the drawer opening.

There are also full-extension side guides that can be used when it is necessary to be able to pull the drawer out to its entire depth, such as on a file cabinet. A full-extension guide is shown in Figure 12-23.

ROLL-OUT TRAYS

A modified drawer, called a roll-out tray, is often used in place of shelves in base cabinets. Since the roll-out tray is normally hidden behind the cabinet doors, the front is not necessarily made to match the cabinet faces but rather is made of the same material as the drawer sides. The front is often narrower than the sides, as shown in Figure 12-24, to provide easy access to the contents. Roll-out trays are usually mounted on side roller guides, but hardwood side guides may also be used. Notice that false partitions are installed just inside the door opening for mounting the roller guides. This allows the trays to be rolled out past the doors even when they are opened only 90°.

CHAPTER 13

Cabinet Cutout and Machining

Cabinet cutout and machining consists of cutting all the parts on the cutting list to finished size and then machining all joints, moldings, and other parts as specified in the shop drawings. Before cutting begins, the cutting list should be studied carefully to determine the best utilization of material. When cutting hardwood plywoods, it is sometimes helpful to sketch the proposed cutting plan on a piece of paper to obtain the best utilization of the 4-ft. by 8-ft. sheet.

Most of the cutting of sheet materials is done on the table saw. Hardwood plywoods are particularly sensitive to chipping when cutting across the face grain, so it is very important that a sharp plywood blade be fitted for cutting sheet material. The table surface, rip fence, and the bars that the rip fence slides on should all be waxed with a hard paste wax and buffed before starting to cut. When running large sheets of plywood or particle board through the saw, any binding caused by friction between the wood and the fence or table surface could cause the wood to bind against the saw blade and be kicked back at the operator. The wood will slide smoothly on the waxed surface, and this also reduces operator fatigue.

MEASUREMENTS AND ACCURACY

Accuracy in measuring is critical in cabinetmaking. Most cabinets have a specific location into which they must fit. It is not uncommon to have three or

Figure 13-1 A table saw with a measuring scale for setting the rip fence. (Courtesy of Biesemeyer Manufacturing Corporation)

four or more cabinets in a row, and the total length of all the cabinets must not vary more than 1/16 in. Each of these cabinets is made of a number of parts that must be cut accurately if the total specified cabinet dimensions are to be maintained.

Many table saws have a measuring scale built into the rail that the rip fence slides on (Figure 13-1). These are very helpful in cabinetmaking because they allow the rip fence to be quickly changed for different-width cuts without shutting off the saw, waiting for the blade to stop, and then measuring the blade-to-fence distance.

They should, however, be checked for accuracy before relying on them for accurate measurement. For instance, any time a different blade is installed, the fence should be adjusted (Figure 13-2).

When the fence must be set by measuring, a steel measuring tape may be used. The tip of the tape is placed against the rip fence, as shown

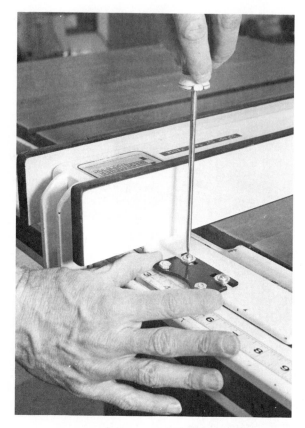

Figure 13-2 "Zeroing" the rip-fence measuring scale

Figure 13-3 Setting the rip fence by measuring

in Figure 13-3 and the tape blade is run directly under a sawtooth that points toward the fence. The actual measurement is taken from the fence side of the tooth. Accuracy here is important because the distance between the inside of the blade and the rip fence determines the size of the part being cut.

HANDLING SHEET MATERIALS ON THE TABLE SAW

Handling and cutting a 4-ft. by 8-ft. sheet of plywood on a table saw is intimidating at first, but it need not be difficult. Most table-saw tops are not large enough to support the sheet completely while it is being cut and after it has been cut into two pieces. A simple rail to the left of the saw and a table behind the saw, as shown in Figure 13-4, can easily be built to allow a person to cut plywood without assistance. This rail and table are at saw-table height and can be moved out of the way when not needed.

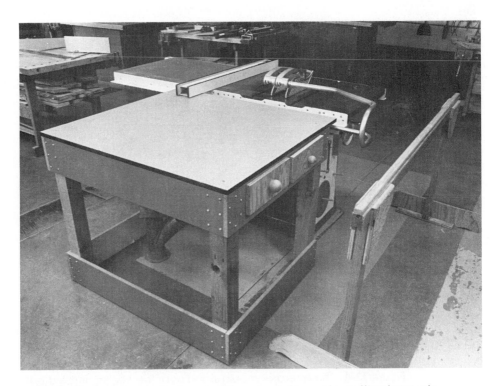

Figure 13-4 A support rail and off-bearing table make cutting large plywood sheets easier.

Figure 13-5 Extended rip fence for a small table saw

Figure 13-6 The operator should stand near the center of the sheet when crosscutting plywood on the table saw. (The saw guard has been removed for clarity in showing this operation.)

On smaller saws it is helpful to extend the rip fence also (Figure 13-5). If the saw is used only for cutting sheet material, a larger table surface may be attached to the saw.

When cutting across the sheet, the operator should stand near the center of the sheet or slightly to the left, as shown in Figure 13-6. The sheet is pushed against the rip fence, and the cut is started. The operator must watch carefully to see that the end of the sheet stays against the rip fence. As the cut is completed, the operator moves toward the rip fence and pushes the piece between the blade and the fence past the back of the blade (Figure 13-7). Just as the cut is completed, the operator reduces the pressure on the part to the left of the blade so that it doesn't bind on the blade.

Making cuts in the long direction of the sheet is much easier. The operator guides the sheet from the back, as shown in Figure 13-8. Again, it is important to see that the edge of the sheet stays firmly against the rip fence.

Figure 13-7 Completing the plywood crosscut. The piece between the blade and the rip fence must be pushed completely past the rear of the blade before it is released.

Figure 13-8 Cutting a plywood sheet in the long direction

CUTTING CABINET PARTS TO SIZE

In this section of the chapter, and in the next section on machining operations, we go step-by-step through the process of cutting out a set of cabinets. The exact sequence of operations may vary somewhat according to the job and the equipment available.

Before cutting is started, the cutting list should be studied carefully. Each cabinet on the list might have some parts that are identical. These should all be cut at the same time to save time in changing the saw settings. Larger parts should generally be cut first; smaller parts are then cut from the remaining material.

As each part is cut, it should be marked on the edge so that it can be easily identified. For instance, a finished end for cabinet A might be marked "A-F.E.," or a partition for cabinet E could be marked "E-Part." As each part is cut and marked, it should be set with other parts for the same cabinet. When all the parts for the job are cut out, there will be a stack of parts for cabinet A, another stack for B, and so on. This makes it easy to find parts for the machining operation to be performed next. It also makes it easy for the person assembling the cabinets if all the parts for each cabinet are grouped together.

MACHINING OPERATIONS

The photographs in Figure 13-9 show most of the common machining operations necessary for a typical set of cabinets.

MACHINING MOLDINGS

While most cabinets have very few molded or shaped surfaces, some of the more ornate cabinets have a number of molded edges typical of those found in some types of fine furniture. Countertops may have a wood molding around the edges, doors and drawer fronts may be shaped, and door panels may be shaped.

Moldings or shaped edges are usually made in the smaller shop with a spindle shaper, a portable router, or an overarm router. Molding may be made on the shaper using cutters manufactured to stock molding patterns such as those shown in Figure 13-10. These are usually available in high-speed

Figure 13-9-a Mitering the front edge of the toe-board cutout on a finished end. Note that the saw blade is set very high for this operation only, to avoid "undercutting" on the back side. The blade should be returned to normal height as soon as this operation is completed.

Figure 13-9-b Cutting the 1/2-in. by 1/2-in. rabbet on the finished end for a base cabinet. (The wall-cabinet finished ends should be run at the same time.)

Figure 13-9-c Notching a partition for the 3/4-in. by 1 1/2-in. nailing strip

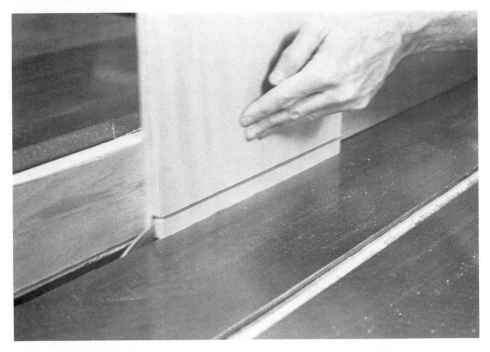

Figure 13-9-d   Rabbeting the wall-cabinet finished end for the cabinet bottom

Figure 13-9-e   Dadoing the finished end for the cabinet top

Figure 13-9-f Cutting the groove for the adjustable shelf standard. Note that these grooves are usually set approximately 1 in. from the front or back of the cabinet for each 10 in. of cabinet depth. The groove for a 12-in.-deep upper cabinet is usually 1 1/4 in. from the front and back of the cabinet.

Figure 13-9-g Cutting the miter joint for joining a finished end to a finished back. Note the piece of scrap wood clamped to the rip fence for the saw blade

Figure 13-9-h Cutting 3/8-in. by 3/4-in. edge banding for shelves and cabinet bottoms. Notice the push stick held against the rip fence and run through the saw to push the thin, 3/8-in. strip past the rear of the blade before releasing it.

steel or carbide, which is more expensive but stays sharp much longer. Flat knives held in place by grooved collars, as shown in Figure 13-11, may also be used. These knives may be ground to any pattern desired. (Accurate knife grinding is very difficult without specialized equipment and is not covered in this book.)

Figure 13-12 shows an edge being molded on the shaper. If a wide laminated board is to have the edges shaped, the end-grain surfaces should always be done first (Figure 13-13). This way, if any splitting occurs at the end of the cut, as it often does on end-grain cutting, the damaged area will usually be cut away when the edge is shaped. It is even a good practice to have the laminated board 1/4 in. to 1/2 in. wider than its finished width before shaping the ends. It can then be cut down to finished width, cutting off any chipped corners before shaping the edges.

The shaper may also be used for shaping curved surfaces when a depth collar is used on the spindle to guide the stock. The collar determines how deep the cutter will be able to cut into the wood. These depth collars are available in incremental sizes to match most cutters. Figure 13-14 shows a depth collar that allows the full molding pattern of the cutter to be used.

Figure 13-10 Three-wing shaper cutters used for making moldings

Figure 13-11 Flat shaper knives held in place with a special set of grooved collars

Figure 13-12 Making a molding on the shaper

When using the shaper to shape a curved surface, a support pin is placed in the table. The stock is supported against this pin and pivoted into the cutter to start the cut (Figure 13-15). As the board comes to rest against the depth collar, the board is moved away from the support pin, and the cut is completed by running the entire edge past the cutter, keeping it against the depth collar.

Portable routers are also often used for machining molded edges. They are especially convenient for use on curved edges since they will easily follow even sharp curves. The router bits used for moldings usually have a pilot bushing that rides against the edge of the board to guide the router, or they may have a pilot bushing that rides against the edge of the board to guide the router, or they may have a small ball bearing for this purpose (Figure 13-16).

To cut a molding with the router, install the desired bit, hold the router flat on the board to be molded, and start the router with the cutter away from the edge. Bring the cutter into the wood until the pilot contacts the edge of the board. Move the router along the edge at a uniform rate, keeping the pilot in contact with the edge of the board (Figure 13-17). Avoid moving too slowly or stopping; the cutter will quickly overheat and burn the wood.

Figure 13-13 Running the end grain first

The normal direction of feed is from left to right as you face the board. However, when it is necessary to run against the grain, chipping can be minimized by going in the other direction. Caution must be observed when doing so because the router will tend to pull itself into the cut. Take a light cut and keep a firm grip on the router.

The overhead or overarm router (Figure 13-18) may also be used for machining molded edges. The same bits may be used except that it is not

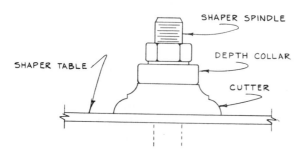

Figure 13-14 Depth collar used on a spindle shaper for shaping curved edges

Figure 13-15 Starting a curved cut using a support pin

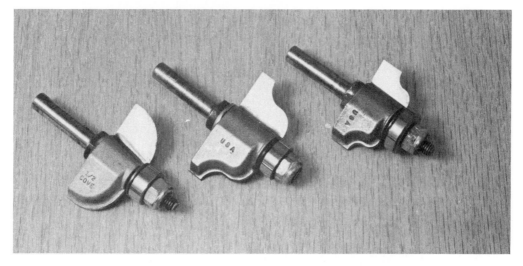

Figure 13-16 Typical router bits for cutting moldings

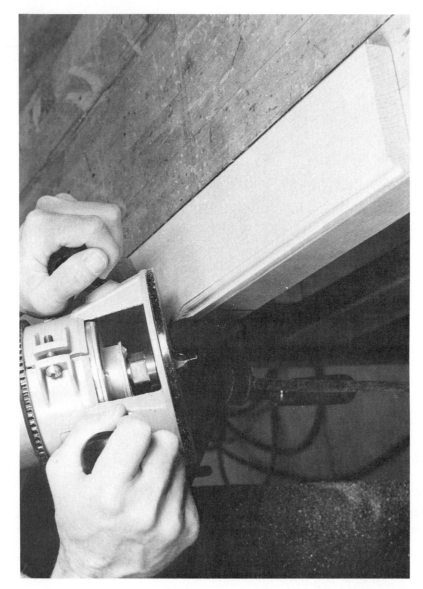

Figure 13-17 Machining a molded edge with a portable router

Figure 13-18   Overarm router

Figure 13-19   Machining a molding on the overarm router

Figure 13-20 Using a guide pin for shaping curved surfaces on the overhead router

necessary to have a pilot on the bit for most operations. Figure 13-19 shows a molding being run on a straight edge with a fence guide clamped to the router table. Notice that the cutter is partially "buried" in the guide fence. This acts as a chip breaker. Curved edges may be routed using the router bit with a pilot or by using a pin in the table under the bit that serves as a guide (Figure 13-20).

MACHINE SAFETY GUIDELINES

Woodworking machines have been improved a great deal in the area of safety in recent years. However, many of them have large, sharp cutters driven by powerful motors and can be dangerous if not used properly. It is probably not possible to list safety rules for every possible operation, but the following guidelines apply to almost all general cutting and machining operations. The equipment manufacturers provide guards with their machines, and while it may occasionally be necessary to remove a guard for a special operation, it should always be replaced immediately upon completion of the operation.

Loose clothing should not be worn when working around machinery.

Long shirttails are especially dangerous around a jointer, for example. Long hair should be confined.

It is always possible that chips, loose knots, or other material may be thrown from a machine, so it is important that safety glasses always be worn while woodworking.

Here are some safety rules that must be observed while operating woodworking machines.

Table Saw

1. Any stock to be cut must have a straight edge to run against the rip fence or to place against the miter gauge.
2. The bottom surface of the stock must be flat to prevent it from rocking and binding on the saw blade.
3. The saw blade should be set only 1/8 in. to 1/4 in. above the stock being cut.
4. A push stick should be used to push narrow stock between the blade and the fence. The stock between the blade and the fence must be pushed past the *rear* of the blade before being released.
5. The rip fence must not be used as a guide when crosscutting with the miter gauge. This will leave the part that has been cut trapped between the fence and the blade, and if it rotates, putting pressure against the side of the blade, it will be kicked back violently.
6. The rip fence should never be used as a guide for cutting across narrow stock.
7. Never cut freehand on the table saw. Always use a rip fence or miter gauge to guide the stock being cut.
8. Do not reach over the moving blade to pick up material.
9. The saw blade should be sharp and of the proper type for the cut being made. A fine-toothed crosscut blade or plywood blade, for example, will overheat and bind in the wood when used for ripping heavy, solid stock and may kick the material out of the machine.

Jointer

1. A push block should always be used when face-jointing boards. Never put your hands directly over the cutters.
2. Stock being jointed must be long enough to span the gap between the infeed and outfeed table safely. The minimum safe length for most jointers is 12 in.
3. Check the depth of cut before starting. A very deep cut, especially when face-jointing, increases the likelihood of a kickback.

Shaper

1. Many shapers have a reversing switch so that the spindle can be rotated in either direction. The rotation direction must always be known, and the stock must be fed against the rotation of the cutter.
2. Whenever possible, the machine should be set up so that the cut is being made on the underside of the stock rather than on the top side.
3. Use spring hold-down guides or feather boards when shaping thin or narrow stock.
4. When shaping a contoured edge using a depth collar, a guide pin in the table must be used for starting the work.
5. Do not use material shorter than 12 in.

Radial-Arm Saw

1. The radial-arm saw, when used for crosscutting, is the only circular woodworking saw that feeds in the direction of blade rotation rather than against the direction of blade rotation. This means that the saw tends to pull itself into the wood, so a very firm grip must be maintained on the saw handle to control the rate of cut.
2. The material being cut should be held firmly against the fence and should lay flat on the table.
3. The saw should be pulled smoothly through the board and fully returned before moving the stock being cut.
4. The radial-arm saw is seldom used for ripping stock in cabinet shops. However, if it is necessary to use it for that purpose, it is imperative that the material be fed *against* the rotation of the blade (from the side opposite the antikickback dogs) and that a push stick be used for narrow cuts. The antikickback dogs must be set at the proper height.

Surface Planer

The surface planer is not a particularly dangerous machine. There are, however, a few safety precautions.

1. If the machine has a solid infeed roll and chip breaker as opposed to a sectional feed roll and chip breaker, only one piece of material should be fed at a time. Otherwise, if two boards of different thickness are fed together, the thicker board will raise the infeed roll and chip breaker, allowing the cutter to kick the thin board back out of the machine.
2. Never get down to look in the machine while it is running. A loose knot or other material could be thrown out.

3. The minimum length of stock that can be planed is determined by the distance between the infeed and outfeed rolls.

Band Saw

1. The sliding upper guide assembly should be set so that the guide is about 1/4 in. above the work.
2. The sequence of cuts should be planned to avoid having to back out of curved cuts. This prevents the likelihood of pulling the blade off the wheels.
3. Round stock should not be cut unless it is held in a clamp or a jig to prevent it from rotating while being cut.
4. Do not cut curves with a radius too small for the width of the blade. This will overheat the blade and cause metal fatigue, leading to early blade breakage.

CHAPTER 14

Face-Frame Cabinet Assembly

Cabinets are usually assembled using glue and pneumatically driven staples and nails. The staples generally have better holding power than nails, but they leave a larger hole in the surface of the wood, so their use is usually restricted to places that are not visible on the finished product. Finish nails are used for attaching face frames to the cabinet and other visible applications where the nail hole must be small and easily filled. Some classes of cabinets, such as Architectural Woodwork Institute premium grade, do not allow nails in face frames.

Pneumatic nailers and staplers have made cabinet assembly much easier and faster. However, there are potential safety hazards involved when using them. The operator's hands should always be well clear of the muzzle. The operator's hands should not be in such a position that they would be hit by a nail deflected out of the board (Figure 14-1). The guns exhaust a blast of air each time they are fired; the operator should know where they exhaust and stay away from that area.

ASSEMBLING THE BASE CABINET

When all the cabinet component parts have been cut and all machine work has been completed, the cabinet is ready for assembly. A large, flat, low (approximately 24 in. high) bench is very convenient for assembling cabinets.

Figure 14-1 Using a pneumatic nailer. Hands must be kept clear in case a nail or staple is deflected out of the wood.

The photographs in Figure 14-2 show the assembly sequence for a typical base cabinet. Most of the photographs show the use of pneumatic staplers and nailers, but the process is the same for hand nailing. Glue is used in all joints.

A 4-in. base block is attached to the finished end to support the cabinet bottom (Figure 14-2-a). The cabinet body is then assembled face down on the bench. The cabinet bottom is attached to the base block on the finished end (Figure 14-2-b). The other end is attached to the cabinet bottom (Figure 14-2-c). If the cabinet has a partition, it is attached to the bottom. Note, if the cabinet has a fixed shelf, the shelf can serve as a spacer to locate the partition, as in the photograph in Figure 14-2-d.

The shelf is then attached to the end and the partition (Figure 14-2-e). Note the 1/4-in. plywood spacers used to locate the shelf at the proper height (usually 11 in. from the bottom of the cabinet).

Figure 14-2-a   Attaching 4-in. base blocks to a finished end

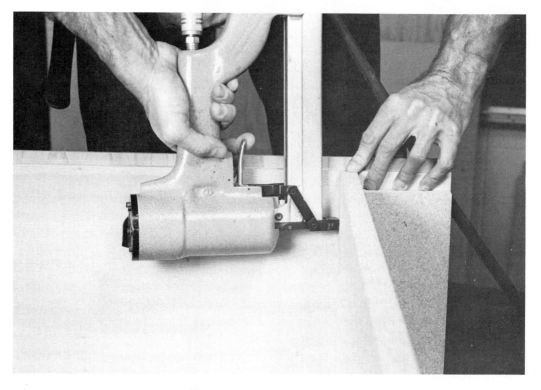

Figure 14-2-b   Attaching the bottom

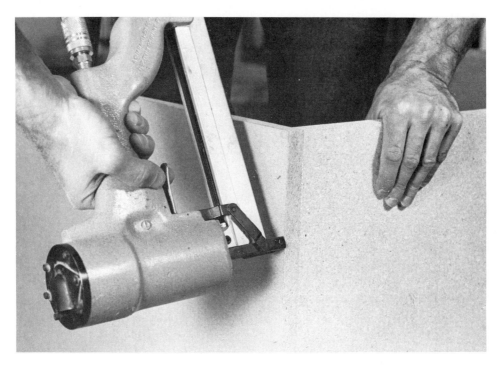

Figure 14-2-c Attaching the other (wall) end to the bottom

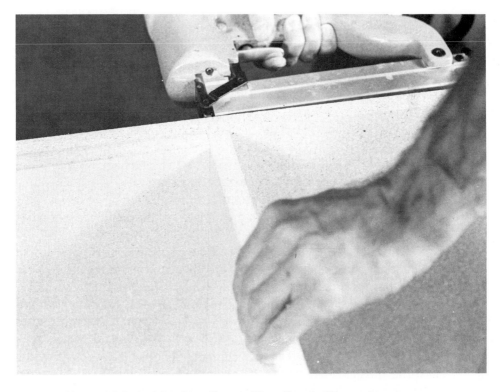

Figure 14-2-d Attaching the partition. The shelf is used as a spacer to locate the partition

Figure 14-2-e Attaching the shelf to the end and the partition using plywood spacers for location

The nailing strip is attached next (Figure 14-2-f). Then the base is assembled (Figure 14-2-g) and attached to the back of the cabinet (Figure 14-2-h). It will be attached to the front of the cabinet later. Note the 2 1/4-in. spacer blocks used to hold the base in position while it is being attached to the cabinet.

The back is attached next (Figure 14-2-i). The back is used to square the cabinet, so the back must be checked for squareness. The back is first nailed or stapled to one end of the cabinet. Then it is pulled up or down as necessary to make its top edge line up with the top edge of the cabinet, as shown in Figure 14-2-j. This squares the cabinet.

The back is then nailed to the cabinet bottom, partition, and fixed shelf. A square or chalk line is used to locate the center of partitions and shelves for nailing purposes (Figure 14-2-k).

The cabinet is now turned over on its back for final assembly. The face frame is attached first (Figure 14-2-l). Great care must be taken to hold the edge of the face frame flush with any finished ends. As soon as the face frame is nailed to the cabinet, the joint between the face frame and the finished end should be examined carefully. If it is not completely tight, it should be clamped for a few minutes, as shown in Figure 14-2-m.

Figure 14-2-f Attaching the nailing strip

Figure 14-2-g Assembling the cabinet base

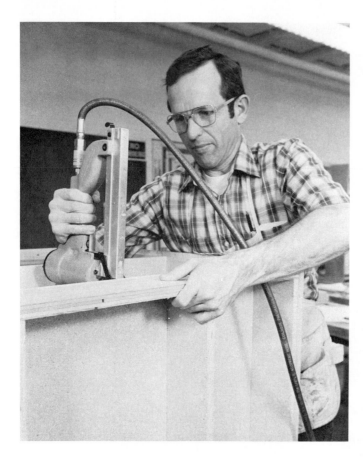

Figure 14-2-h Attaching the base to the back side of the cabinet

Figure 14-2-i Attaching the cabinet back to one end of the cabinet

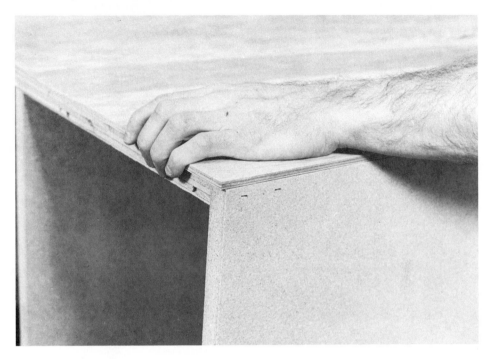

Figure 14-2-j Using the back to square the cabinet

Figure 14-2-k Using a square to locate the center of the partition for nailing

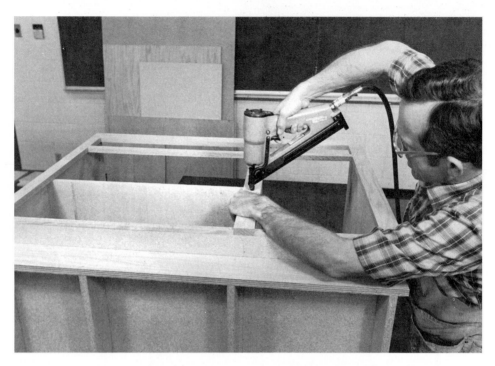

Figure 14-2-l Attaching the face frame

Figure 14-2-m Clamping the
face frame to the cabinet
body

Figure 14-2-n Applying edge banding

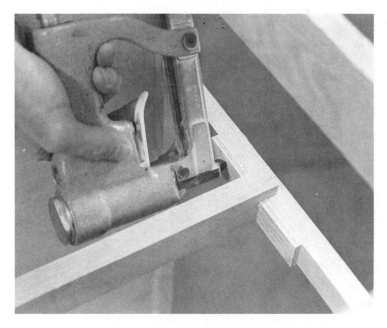

Figure 14-2-o Attaching drawer guides

Figure 14-2-p   Attaching plastic guide tabs

Figure 14-2-q   Attaching the tip rail

Figure 14-2-r Filling nail holes

It is very important that the joint be very tight, since it will be highly visible.

The edge banding is now applied to the front edges of the cabinet bottom and shelves (Figure 14-2-n). This edge banding is 3/8 in. thick if lip doors are to be used and 3/4 in. thick for overlay doors.

If center drawer guides are used, they may be attached now (Figure 14-2-o). See Chapter 12 for details on drawer guides.

The plastic guide tabs are attached to the face frame on either side of the drawer opening (Figure 14-2-p).

The tip rail for top drawers is attached next (Figure 14-2-q).

All nail holes are then filled with a wood filler (Figure 14-2-r).

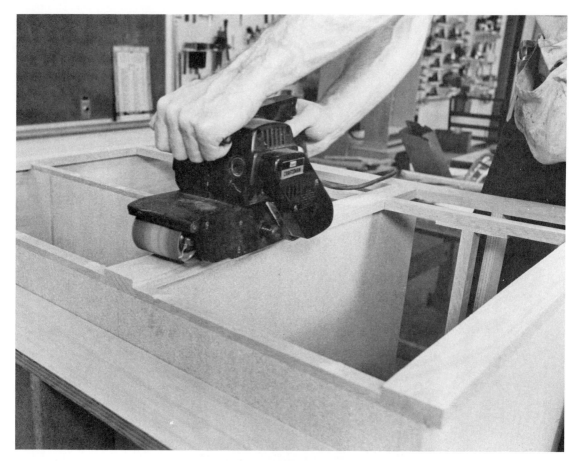

Figure 14-3   Belt-sanding the face frame

SANDING THE CABINET

The cabinet is then sanded. A portable belt sander may be used for the preliminary sanding and to level face-frame joints if the face frame was not previously sanded with a wide-belt sander (Figure 14-3). Great care must be exercised when using the portable belt sander. It is very easy to dig gouges into the wood if it is not held perfectly flat. All cross-grain scratches should be removed with the belt sander.

The face-frame-to-cabinet joint should be carefully sanded (Figure 14-4). Be careful not to sand through the plywood veneer. The cabinet is then completely sanded with a finish sander (Figure 14-5). All sharp edges should be slightly eased with a sanding block (Figure 14-6).

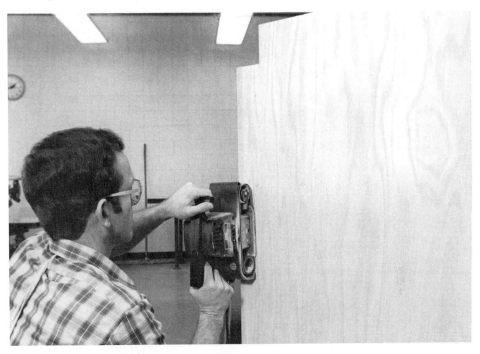

Figure 14-4 Sanding the face-frame joint on the cabinet finished end

Figure 14-5 Final sanding with a finish sander

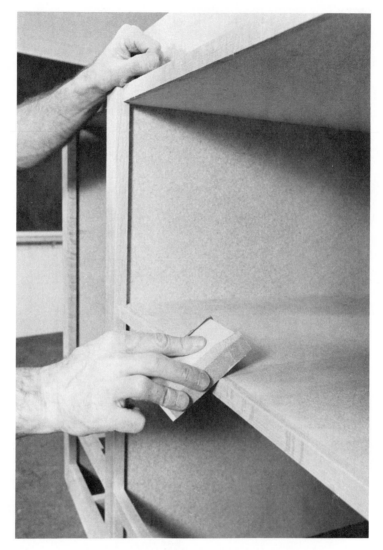

Figure 14-6 Easing sharp edges with a sanding block

INSTALLING DRAWERS

Drawers are installed by sliding the drawer into the opening while supporting the drawer guide (Figure 14-7). When the rear of the drawer guide is positioned for best drawer fit, an assistant can drive a staple or nail through the back of the cabinet into the guide. This may later be reinforced with wood screws.

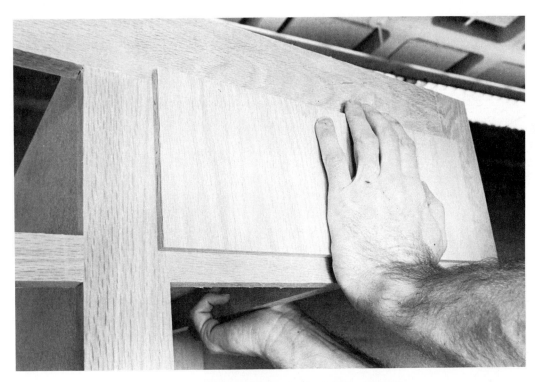

Figure 14-7 Fitting the drawer

HANGING DOORS

The doors are mounted with the cabinet lying on its back on the bench. First the hinges are mounted on the doors (Figure 14-8). Next, the doors are set in the proper opening in the cabinet and lined up flush with the bottom of the cabinet (Figure 14-9).

The doors are then attached to the cabinet (Figure 14-10).

The operation of hanging doors may vary with different types of hinges and doors. The hinge manufacturer's directions should be followed.

If roll-out trays are to be installed, they may be done now. The roller-guide track is often mounted on the cabinet partitions before the cabinet is assembled.

ASSEMBLING THE WALL CABINET

The series of photographs in Figure 14-11 shows the assembly of a wall cabinet. Following this sequence, the nail holes are filled, the cabinet is sanded, and the doors are hung, just as on the base cabinet. The doors are sometimes left off wall cabinets until they have been installed, to make it easier to lift the cabinet into place.

(a)

(b)

Figure 14-8 Mounting hinges on the door. Notice the hinge jig used to mark the location of the screw holes.

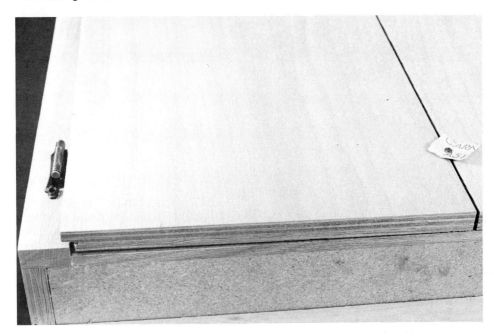

Figure 14-9 Positioning the doors in the cabinet opening. Notice the nails used as spacers between the pair of doors.

Figure 14-10 Attaching the doors to the cabinet

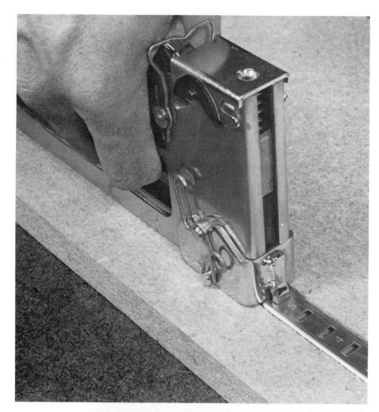

Figure 14-11-a Installing an adjustable shelf standard. The adjustable shelf standards are installed before the cabinet is assembled. These must be numbered in groups of four for each opening and must be installed with the numbers reading right side up. They may be installed with special nails or with staples, using a stapler made for this purpose as shown here.

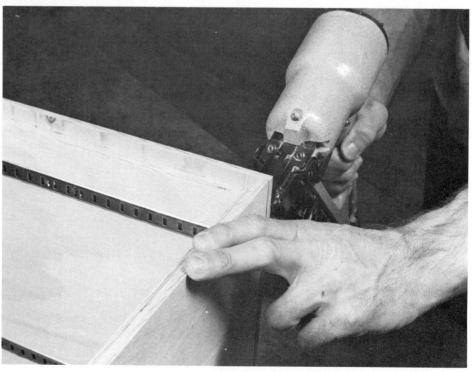

Figure 14-11-b The ends are then attached.

Figure 14-11-c The nailing strip is attached.

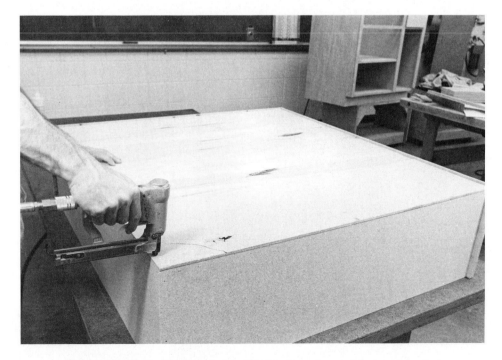

Figure 14-11-d The back is attached and used to square the cabinet, as on the base cabinet.

Figure 14-11-e   The cabinet is turned over, and the face frame and edge banding are attached.

Figure 14-11-f   Adjustable shelves are edge-banded and nail holes are filled and sanded. Notice the V block used to hold them in position for edge banding and sanding.

SECTION FOUR

Computers

Computers have several important applications in a modern cabinet-making business. They can be used as a sales tool by virtue of their capability of producing perspective drawings of kitchens for customers. They can also produce quick and accurate price estimates.

Computers can also be used to design cabinets, produce shop drawings, generate cutting lists, and even determine the most efficient way to cut cabinet parts from sheet material.

Section four (Chapter 15) describes these applications and shows some examples for both frameless and face-frame systems.

CHAPTER 15

Computer Applications

Along with the introduction of the frameless cabinet system, the other revolution in cabinetmaking in the United States has been the introduction and rapid acceptance of the use of computers.

In addition to the normal business-related functions, computers can be used to design cabinets, produce perspective drawings for customers, produce shop drawings, generate cutting lists, determine the best way to cut parts from a panel, and even control the panel-cutting saw. Computers also save time and increase accuracy in estimating and bidding.

Even though computers and software are quite expensive, the payback time is generally considered to be much faster for computers than for any other type of shop equipment.

ESTIMATING AND SALES APPLICATIONS

Computers can be a great help in selling cabinet jobs because they can produce perspective drawings that help customers visualize the appearance of the kitchen from any angle. They can experiment with different cabinet arrangements and quickly see the results. In practice, the floor plan is drawn first, starting with the walls and including window and door locations. The sink and appliance locations are then determined and the base cabinets are drawn in the remaining space. Finally, the wall cabinets are drawn. At this point a drawing can be generated on a plotter or a printer. A computer-generated floor-plan drawing is shown in Figure 15-1.

The computer will then generate elevation drawings of each wall from the floor plan, using operator-provided information about door, drawer, shelf, and general cabinet configuration. The wall-elevation drawings can be used to show the customer what the cabinet and appliance arrangement for each wall as well as any island or peninsula cabinets will look like. A typical wall-elevation drawing from the previously generated floor plan is shown in Figure 15-2.

At this point many computer programs allow the development of a perspective drawing from any point in the room, looking in any direction. This is probably one of the most helpful sales tools because the perspective drawing is similar to a photograph in terms of cabinet shape and size relationships.

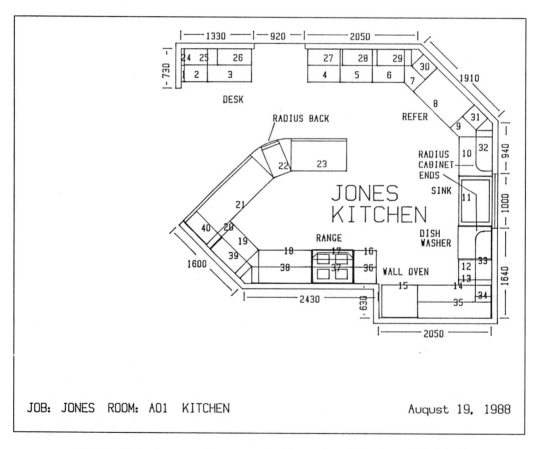

Figure 15-1 A computer-generated floor plan. (Courtesy of Cabinetware, Inc.)

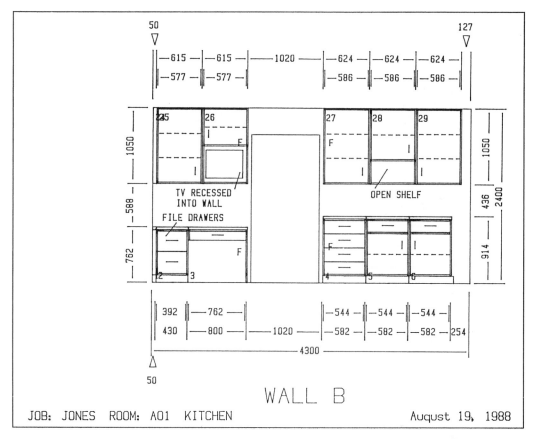

Figure 15-2 A computer-generated wall-elevation drawing. (Courtesy of Cabinetware, Inc.)

A perspective drawing allows the customer to visualize thé proposed kitchen without the need to learn to interpret shop-type drawings. A perspective drawing from the previously shown floor plan is shown in Figure 15-3.

Some programs allow shading to produce a color rendering of the kitchen. In fact, computer programs are available that can create a library of color images of cabinet components (doors, etc.) appliances, countertop materials, floor coverings, and so forth, with a video camera. These elements can then be incorporated into the cabinet perspective drawing, allowing you to show the customer a "photograph" of the kitchen that doesn't yet exist! Most computer programs will produce drawings for either frameless-style cabinets, as shown in Figures 15-1, 15-2, and 15-3, or face-frame cabinets, as shown in Figures 15-4, 15-5, and 15-6.

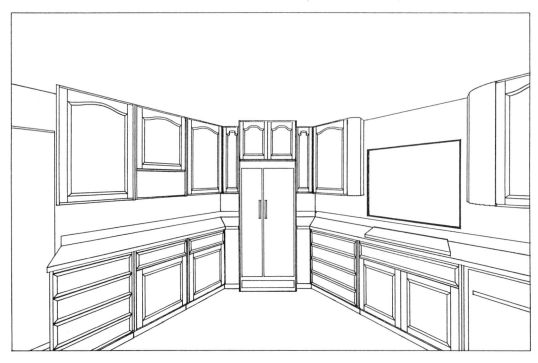

Figure 15-3 A computer-generated perspective drawing. (Courtesy of Cabinetware, Inc.)

Computers can also help sell cabinet jobs by allowing you to quickly supply the customer with price proposals or bids. This also saves the shop a great deal of money and time because the time required to prepare a bid is reduced dramatically, and there is less chance of error.

Price estimating can be done by the linear foot, square foot, price per box, or material and labor. A common way of pricing cabinets for customers is by linear foot of cabinet for the cabinet boxes and then adding a certain amount for each drawer box, square foot of door (different door types are priced differently), square foot of drawer front, Lazy Susan units, and any other special feature.

The estimate is automatically compiled from the previously completed computer drawings. Figure 15-7 shows a typical bid proposal generated from the drawings shown in Figures 15-4 to 15-6. A detailed bid report for the use of the cabinet shop can be printed. Such a report is shown in Figure 15-8.

Needless to say, it is very important that someone keep all prices used in the bidding program up to date. Any increases or decreases in the price of hardware, material, or labor must be entered immediately if the bid is to be accurate.

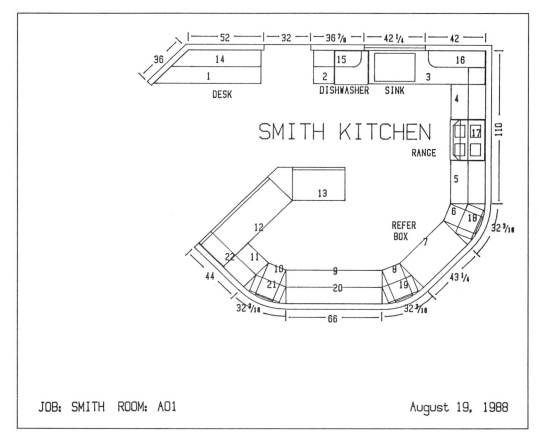

Figure 15-4 A computer-generated floor plan for face-frame cabinets. (Courtesy of Cabinetware, Inc.)

SHOP APPLICATIONS

The main shop applications for computers are in producing shop drawings, generating parts-cutting lists, and, in some cases, generating panel-cutting plans.

From the elevation drawings shown in Figures 15-2 and 15-5, a detailed shop drawing of each cabinet can be generated. This drawing might be an oblique drawing, an orthographic projection front view, a cross-section view, or some combination. The drawings can usually be made with either a dot-matrix printer or a plotter.

These shop drawings are used to show the people in the shop how the cabinets are assembled and any special machining that may be necessary. Architects sometimes require that shop drawings be submitted for approval

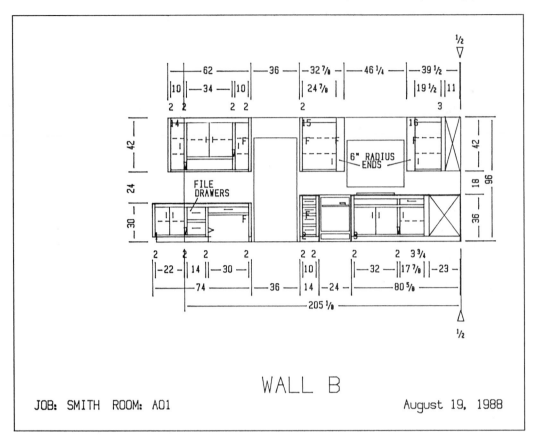

Figure 15-5 A computer-generated wall-elevation drawing for face-frame cabinets. (Courtesy of Cabinetware, Inc.)

before construction is started, so these drawings can be used for that purpose as well. Shop drawings contain information about cabinet size, door and drawer size and location, door-hinge side, shelf location, finished-end designation, and general construction details.

One of the most useful shop applications for the computer is the generation of parts-cutting lists. These cutting lists are generated from the shop drawings. Three general types of cutting lists are generated. These include parts list for the cabinet boxes, drawer-cutting lists, and door-cutting lists. A face-frame cutting list is generated for face-frame versions. In addition to generating cutting lists, some programs will generate and print labels for each part to be used to identify parts for the person assembling the cabinet.

Some programs will generate cutting lists in three different forms: master, grouped or batched, and individual. The master cutting list specifies

Figure 15-6 A computer-generated perspective drawing for face-frame cabinets. (Courtesy of Cabinetware, Inc.)

the size of each cabinet part required for the entire job. Such a list is shown in Figure 15-9. A batched list for the same job, in which all parts of the same size and material are batched together, is shown in Figure 15-10.

Finally, an individual cutting list along with a drawing of the cabinet is shown in Figure 15-11. The main use of the individual list is for the person assembling the cabinet. The master and batched lists are very valuable to the person or persons cutting out the cabinets.

Most programs will also generate cabinet-door cutting lists. If the doors are to be slab doors cut from sheet material, the list will just show width and height plus any other needed information. For frame-and-panel doors, the list will also show the sizes of all stiles, rails, and panels. Such a list is shown in Figure 15-12.

Similarly, drawer-parts cutting lists can also be generated, as shown in Figure 15-13.

Cutting lists for the face-frame cabinets shown in Figures 15-4 to 15-6 are shown in Figures 15-14 to 15-18.

For frameless cabinets, a computer-generated, hole-mounting information sheet (Figure 15-19) is very helpful. It shows where to mount hinges on

PROPOSAL April 21, 1988

Bingham Wood Products, Inc.
Rt. 2 Box 2490
Davis, CA 95616
Lic No 234567

CRC Construction
6276 F St.
Davis, CA 95616

John Smith
1237 N 10th St.
Davis, CA 95616

We propose to perform the following work in accordance with the drawings and specifications submitted and completed in a workmanlike manner according to standard for the sum listed below as "TOTAL", with payments to be made listed below as "TERMS".

KITCHEN
EXTERIOR WOOD: OAK
INTERIOR WOOD: MELAMINE
DOOR STYLE: RAISED PANEL

BASE	30.22	lineal feet	$2007.50
UPPER	28.91	lineal feet	$1446.65
FLOOR-TO-CEILING	46.69	square feet	$771.18
PEN BASE	8.55	lineal feet	$647.30
DRAWER BOXES	19		$588.85
DOORS	139.73	square feet	$2667.26
DRAWER FRONTS	16.38	square feet	$154.74
SINK TRAY	1		$22.73
4x8 LIGHT BOX	1		$189.39
CROWN MOULDING	33	lineal feet	$100.00
2 1/4" BASE BOARD	46	lineal feet	$87.12
			=====
		SUBTOTAL:	$8682.72
		SALES TAX:	$520.96
			=====
		TOTAL:	$9203.68

TERMS: 50% DEPOSIT - REMAINDER UPON COMPLETION
BID GOOD UNTIL: July 21, 1988

Any alteration or deviation from the above specifications involving extra costs will be made only upon written agrement, and will become an extra charge over and above the estimate. This proposal may be withdrawn by us at any time before acceptance.

Authorized Signature:____________________

ACCEPTANCE OF PROPOSAL
The above prices, specifications and conditions are satisfactory and are hereby accepted. You are authorized to do the work as specified. Payments will be made as outlined above. It is understood and agreed that this is work not provided for in any other agreement and no contractual rights arise until this proposal is accepted in writing.

Date:________________ Signature:____________________

======================================Page 1=======

Figure 15-7 A computer-generated bid proposal for the cabinets shown in Figures 15-4 to 15-6. (Courtesy of Cabinetware, Inc.)

BID REPORT

BID: SMITH   ORIGINAL BID   April 21, 1988

Item	QUANTITY	LABOR	MATERIAL	HIDDEN	RESULT	OVERHEAD	PROFIT	TOTAL
		PRICE LIST: FRAME						
KITCHEN								
EXTERIOR: OAK								
INTERIOR: BIRCH								
DOOR: RAISED PANEL								
BASE	30.22	906.60	418.35	0.00	1324.95	321.20	361.35	2007.50
UPPER	28.91	578.20	376.59	0.00	954.79	231.46	260.40	1446.65
FTOC	46.69	373.52	135.46	0.00	508.98	123.39	138.81	771.18
PEN BASE	8.55	299.34	127.88	0.00	427.22	103.57	116.51	647.30
DRAWER BOXES	19	285.00	103.64	0.00	388.64	94.22	105.99	588.85
DOORS	139.73	1397.30	363.09	0.00	1760.39	426.76	480.11	2667.26
DRAWER FRONTS	16.38	32.76	69.37	0.00	102.13	24.76	27.85	154.74
SINK TRAY	1			0.00	15.00	3.64	4.09	22.73
4x8 LIGHT BOX	1			0.00	125.00	30.30	34.09	189.39
CROWN MOULDING	33			0.00	66.00	16.00	18.00	100.00
2 1/4" BASE BOARD	46			0.00	57.50	13.94	15.68	87.12
		3872.72	1594.38	0.00	5730.60	1389.24	1562.88	8682.72
					5730.60	1389.24	1562.88	8682.72

SALES TAX APPL. TO: 8682.72   (6.00%)

NONTAXABLE TOTAL   0.00

SALES TAX   520.96

TOTAL   9203.68

Figure 15-8 A computer-generated detailed bid report for cabinet-shop use. (Courtesy of Cabinetware, Inc.)

doors, which system holes to use for mounting hinge plates, and which system holes to use for mounting drawer guides.

A material cost list (Figure 15-20) is also available with some programs.

Panel-cutting optimization is another major function available for computers. Panel-cutting optimization programs start with the cutting list and then determine the best way to cut the parts from large panels to give the best material yield. Traditionally this job has been done by the saw operator. The saw operator was given a cutting list and would then mentally try to calculate the best way to cut the part from the sheets available. This works reasonably well for small jobs that require only one or two sheets,

MASTER CUTTING LIST

FOR BODY PARTS

March 15, 1988   BINGHAM WOOD PRODUCTS   Page 2
                                        JONES CUTTING LIST

BODIES

Number of Pieces	Width	Length		Cabinet Number	Section Number	Description	

==

Material: 3/4 1S MELAMINE
Special operations: BORE FOR SYSTEM HOLES

Number of Pieces	Width	Length		Cabinet Number	Section Number	Description	
1	610	1081.5	1L	A01-14	1	BOTTOM	
1	610	914	1L	A01-11	1	TOP	
1	610	904	1L	A01-7	1	BOTTOM	
1	610	876	1L	A01-4	1	BOTTOM	
1	610	862	1L	A01-15	1	BOTTOM	
1	610	774	1L	A01-3		RIGHT END	WALL
1	610	774	1L	A01-4		LEFT END	WALL
1	610	774	1L	A01-4		RIGHT END	WALL
1	610	774	1L	A01-5		LEFT END	WALL
1	610	774	1L	A01-5		RIGHT END	WALL
1	610	774	1L	A01-7		LEFT END	WALL
1	610	774	1L	A01-8		RIGHT END	WALL
1	610	774	1L	A01-10		LEFT END	WALL
1	610	774	1L	A01-10		RIGHT END	WALL
1	610	774	1L	A01-12		LEFT END	WALL
1	610	774	1L	A01-12		RIGHT END	WALL
1	610	774	1L	A01-14		LEFT END	WALL
1	610	654.5	1L	A01-8	1	BOTTOM	
1	610	518.5	1L	A01-5	1	BOTTOM	
1	610	427.5	1L	A01-3	1	BOTTOM	
1	610	363	1L	A01-1	1	BOTTOM	
1	610	266.5	1L	A01-12	1	BOTTOM	
1	610	254.5	1L	A01-10	1	BOTTOM	
1	610	136	1L	A01-2		LEFT END	WALL

15.77 m. = 6.47 rip(s)

Material: 3/4 2S MELAMINE

Number of Pieces	Width	Length		Cabinet Number	Section Number	Description
1	582	911	1L	A01-11	1	ADJ SHELF
1	582	901	1L	A01-7	1	ADJ SHELF
1	582	651.5	1L	A01-8	1	ADJ SHELF
1	582	528	1L	A01-14	1	ADJ SHELF
1	582	528	1L	A01-14	1	ADJ SHELF
1	582	515.5	1L	A01-15	1	ADJ SHELF
1	582	263.5	1L	A01-12	1	ADJ SHELF
1	582	251.5	1L	A01-10	1	ADJ SHELF

4.55 m. = 2.24 rip(s)

Figure 15-9   A computer-generated master cutting list. (Courtesy of Cabinetware, Inc.)

BATCHED CUTTING LIST

FOR BODY PARTS

March 15, 1988   BINGHAM WOOD PRODUCTS   Page 2
                                          JONES CUTTING LIST

BODIES
Number
of Pieces   Width   Length   Description   Room #Cabinet (Quantity)
= =

                              Material: 3/4 1S MELAMINE
                              Special operations: BORE FOR SYSTEM HOLES

1	610	1081.5	1L	BOTTOM	A01[#14(1)]
1	610	914	1L	TOP	A01[#11(1)]
1	610	904	1L	BOTTOM	A01[#7(1)]
1	610	876	1L	BOTTOM	A01[#4(1)]
1	610	862	1L	BOTTOM	A01[#15(1)]
12	610	774	1L	END	A01[#3(1) #4(2) #5(2) #7(1) #8(1) #10(2) #12(2) #14(1)]
1	610	654.5	1L	BOTTOM	A01[#8(1)]
1	610	518.5	1L	BOTTOM	A01[#5(1)]
1	610	427.5	1L	BOTTOM	A01[#3(1)]
1	610	363	1L	BOTTOM	A01[#1(1)]
1	610	266.5	1L	BOTTOM	A01[#12(1)]
1	610	254.5	1L	BOTTOM	A01[#10(1)]
1	610	136	1L	END	A01[#2(1)]

          15.77 m. = 6.47 rip(s)

                              Material: 3/4 2S MELAMINE

1	582	911	1L	ADJ SHELF	A01[#11(1)]
1	582	901	1L	ADJ SHELF	A01[#7(1)]
1	582	651.5	1L	ADJ SHELF	A01[#8(1)]
2	582	528	1L	ADJ SHELF	A01[#14(1)]
1	582	515.5	1L	ADJ SHELF	A01[#15(1)]
1	582	263.5	1L	ADJ SHELF	A01[#12(1)]
1	582	251.5	1L	ADJ SHELF	A01[#10(1)]

          4.55 m. = 2.24 rip(s)

- All Parts Of The Same Material Are Grouped Together
- Any Special Machining Operations Are Listed For Each Part
- A Full Description Of Each Part Is Listed Including The Room Number, Cabinet Number And Part Name
- Like Width Parts Are Listed From Longest To Shortest
- Like Size Parts Are Grouped Together
- All Material And Part Names Are Printed Using Your Own Terminology
- The Number Of Rips Out Of A Sheet Of Material At A Specific Width Is Listed
- The Number Of Edges To Be Edgebanded Is Listed For Each Part
- Using The Batched Cutlist Option, Like Size Parts Are Grouped Together For Efficient Cutout, Thereby Decreasing The Amount Of Paperwork

Figure 15-10 A computer-generated batched cutting list. (Courtesy of Cabinetware, Inc.)

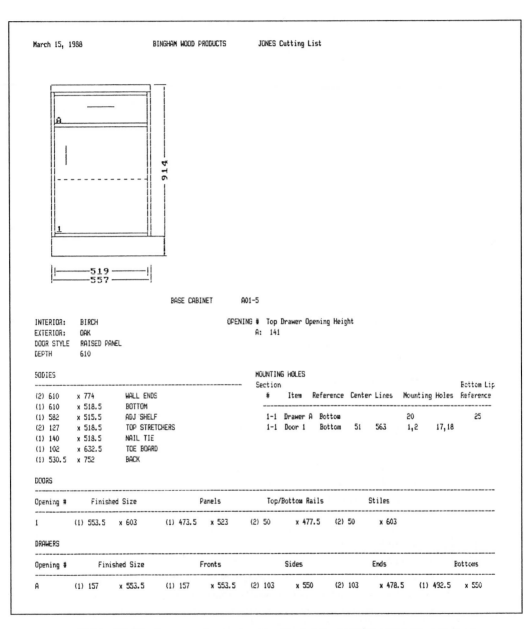

Figure 15-11 A computer-generated individual cutting list with cabinet drawing. (Courtesy of Cabinetware, Inc.)

DOOR CUTTING LIST

March 15, 1988   BINGHAM WOOD PRODUCTS   Page 3
                                              JONES CUTTING LIST

FRAME AND PANEL DOORS

Finished Size (WxH)	Panel (WxH)	Top/Bottom Rails (WxL)	Stiles (WxL)	Room/Cabinet-Door

Panel Type: 4/4 SOLID OAK   Style: RAISED PANEL

Finished Size (WxH)	Panel (WxH)	Top/Bottom Rails (WxL)	Stiles (WxL)	Room/Cabinet-Door
2) 556.5x603	2) 476.5x523	4) 50x480.5	4) 50x603	A01[#14-1,2]
1) 556.5x603	1) 473.5x523	2) 50x477.5	2) 50x603	A01[#5-1]
2) 556.5x603	2) 374x523	4) 50x378	4) 50x603	A01[#4-1]
2) 556.5x1627	2) 367x1547	4) 50x371	4) 50x1627	A01[#15-1]
2) 556.5x603	2) 263x523	4) 50x267	4) 50x603	A01[#8-1]
2) 556.5x603	2) 221.5x523	4) 50x225.5	2) 50x603	A01[#12-1]
2) 556.5x603	2) 209.5x523	4) 50x213.5	2) 50x603	A01[#10-1]
2) 556.5x603	2) 197.5x523	4) 50x201.5	2) 50x603	A01[#7-1]

- A Complete Cutlist Is Printed Out For Four Different Door Styles; Slab Doors With Or Without Edgebanding, Frame And Panel Doors, Buy Out Doors And Frame And Panel Doors With Matching Drawer Fronts
- The Overall Door Size For Each Door Is Listed
- The Hinging For Each Door Is Listed
- Each Door Is Identified By A Room Number, Cabinet Number And Door Number
- Like Width Parts Are Listed From Longest To Shortest
- Like Size Parts Are Grouped Together

Figure 15-12 A computer-generated cutting list for frame-and-panel doors. (Courtesy of Cabinetware, Inc.)

but it is very inefficient for large jobs, especially if there are many part sizes to be cut.

Panel-cutting optimization programs are usually integrated with programs that generate cutting lists, so that the cutting list can be fed directly into the optimization program. The optimization program then calculates the best way to cut the parts from the available sheets. A cutting diagram, such as the one shown in Figure 15-21, can then be printed or plotted. The program takes into consideration saw kerf thickness, edge-trimming requirements, and grain direction, if necessary. (You can specify which way you want the grain direction to run on parts cut from grained material.)

DRAWER CUTTING LIST

March 15, 1988   BINGHAM WOOD PRODUCTS   Page 4
                                              JONES CUTTING LIST

DRAWERS

Fronts (HxW)	Sides (WxL)	Ends (WxL)	Bottoms (WxL)	Room/Cabinet-Drawer

Front Type:4/4 SOLID OAK   Door Style:RAISED PANEL   Interior:19mm MEL   Slide Type:BLUM 230e SLIDES

Fronts (HxW)	Sides (WxL)	Ends (WxL)	Bottoms (WxL)	Room/Cabinet-Drawer
1) 300.5x746	2) 249.5x559	2) 249.5x672	1) 686x559	A01[#11-D]
3) 284x746	6) 249.5x559	6) 249.5x672	3) 686x559	A01[#11-A,B,C]
1) 218x516	2) 167x559	2) 167x442	1) 456x559	A01[#1-D]
2) 188x516	4) 135x559	4) 135x442	2) 456x559	A01[#1-B,C]
2) 156x516	4) 103x559	4) 103x442	2) 456x559	A01[#4-A/#5-A]
2) 156x516	4) 103x559	4) 103x442	2) 456x559	A01[#1-A/#2-A]
1) 156x417	2) 103x559	2) 103x343	1) 357x559	A01[#9-A]
2) 156x393	4) 103x559	4) 103x319	2) 333x559	A01[#6-A/#7-A]
1) 156x304.5	2) 103x559	2) 103x230.5	1) 244.5x559	A01[#8-A]

- Each Drawer Is Identified By A Room Number, Cabinet Number And Drawer Number
- Like Width Parts Are Listed From Longest To Shortest
- Like Size Parts Are Grouped Together

Figure 15-13 A computer-generated drawer-cutting list. (Courtesy of Cabinetware, Inc.)

Most panel-cutting optimization programs can be run to give the ultimate best material yield, or they can be run to emphasize saving labor in cutting. When the program's panel-cutting plan is shown on the screen, it also reports the percentage yield (or percentage of waste). For example, if you were to run the program for maximum labor efficiency, you could see what the material yield would be. If the waste factor was too high, you could run the program again emphasizing material yield and then see if the savings in material would offset the extra labor needed to cut the material.

The decision to emphasize labor or material may depend upon the type of panel-cutting saw being used. For example, a horizontal, computer-con-

MASTER CUTTING LIST

FOR BODY PARTS

June 9, 1987   BINGHAM WOOD PRODUCTS   Page 2
                                             SMITH CUTTING LIST

BODIES

Number of Pieces	Width	Length	Cabinet Number	Section Number	Description	

Material:3/4 A2 OAK VENEER
Special Operations: DADO FOR BACK

Number of Pieces	Width	Length	Cabinet Number	Section Number	Description	
1	23-1/4	95-1/2	A01-7		LEFT END	FINISH
1	23-1/4	95-1/2	A01-7		RIGHT END	FINISH
1	23-1/4	95-1/2	A01-10		LEFT END	FINISH
1	23-1/4	95-1/2	A01-10		RIGHT END	FINISH
1	23-1/4	30-1/2	A01-2		LEFT END	FINISH
1	23-1/4	26-1/2	A01-1		LEFT END	FINISH
1	23-1/4	26-1/2	A01-1		RIGHT END	FINISH

38.79 ft. = 4.85 rip(s)

Material: 5/8 1S MELAMINE

Number of Pieces	Width	Length	Cabinet Number	Section Number	Description	
1	23	64	A01-3	1	BOTTOM	
1	23	53-15/16	A01-9	1	BOTTOM	
1	23	39-7/8	A01-4	1	BOTTOM	
1	23	38-13/16	A01-7	1	TOP	
1	23	31-5/8	A01-1	1	BOTTOM	
1	23	30-1/2	A01-2		RIGHT END	WALL
1	23	30-1/2	A01-3		LEFT END	WALL
1	23	30-1/2	A01-3		RIGHT END	WALL
1	23	30-1/2	A01-4		LEFT END	WALL
1	23	30-1/2	A01-5		RIGHT END	WALL
1	23	30-1/2	A01-6		LEFT END	WALL
1	23	30-1/2	A01-6		RIGHT END	WALL
1	23	30-1/2	A01-8		LEFT END	WALL
1	23	30-1/2	A01-8		RIGHT END	WALL
1	23	30-1/2	A01-9		LEFT END	WALL
1	23	30-1/2	A01-9		RIGHT END	WALL
1	23	28-13/16	A01-10	1	BOTTOM	
1	23	28-13/16	A01-10	1	TOP	
1	23	23-7/16	A01-5	1	BOTTOM	
1	23	17-3/8	A01-2	1	BOTTOM	
1	23	14-13/16	A01-1	1	BOTTOM	
1	23	12-7/16	A01-6	1	BOTTOM	
1	23	11-15/16	A01-8	1	BOTTOM	

63.54 ft. = 7.94 rip(s)

- All Parts Of The Same Material Are Grouped Together
- Any Special Machining Operations Are Listed For Each Part
- A Full Description Of Each Part Is Listed Including The Room Number, Cabinet Number And Part Name
- Like Width Parts Are Listed From Longest To Shortest
- Like Size Parts Are Grouped Together
- All Material And Part Names Are Printed Using Your Own Terminology
- The Number Of Rips Out Of A Sheet Of Material At A Specific Width Is Listed

Figure 15-14 A computer-generated cutting list for the face-frame cabinets shown in Figures 15-4 to 15-6. (Courtesy of Cabinetware, Inc.)

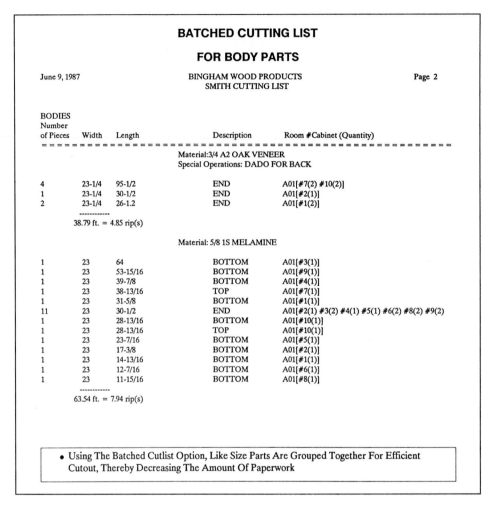

Figure 15-15 A computer-generated batched cutting list. (Courtesy of Cabinetware, Inc.)

trolled panel saw with automatic panel loading requires relatively little labor per cut, so you would optimize for material yield. On the other hand, a shop with a vertical panel saw or a sliding table saw might elect to optimize favoring labor because sheets may have to be picked up and turned between cuts when changing from rips to crosscuts.

One of the larger cabinetmaking software companies offers panel-cutting optimization programs in several levels, depending on the quantity of panel cutting that a shop does. A program designed for a small company doing custom jobs would generate a program that gives the exact number of parts needed, in a format that could be cut on a table saw or a vertical

BATCHED CUTTING LIST

FACE FRAMES

June 9, 1987   BINGHAM WOOD PRODUCTS   Page 3
SMITH CUTTING LIST

FACE FRAMES
Number

of Pieces	Width	Length	Description	Room #Cabinet (Quantity)
			Material:4/4 SOLID OAK	
1	4	85	TOP RAIL	A01[#14(1)]
1	4	57	TOP RAIL	A01[#17(1)]
1	4	44	TOP RAIL	A01[#11(1)]
1	4	36	TOP RAIL	A01[#7(1)]
1	4	33-7/8	TOP RAIL	A01[#12(1)]
1	4	32-3/4	TOP RAIL	A01[#13(1)]
1	4	26	TOP RAIL	A01[#10(1)]
2	4	15	TOP RAIL	A01[#15(1) #16(1)]
		28.73 ft.		
2	2	95-1/2	STILE	A01#7(2)]
2	2	91-1/2	STILE	A01#10(2)]
1	2	60-3/8	RAIL	A01#3(2)]
1	2	52-1/16	RAIL	A01#9(2)]
1	2	44	RAIL	A01#11(2)]
8	2	42	STILE	A01#11(2) #12(2) #13(1) #15(1) #16(1) #17(1)]
2	2	38	MULLION	A01#14(2)]
1	2	36-1/2	MULLION	A01#17(1)]
8	2	31-1/4	STILE	A01#2(2) #3(2) #4(1) #5(1) #6(1) #8(1) #9(1)]
1	2	29-1/4	STILE	A01[#1(1)]
1	2	26	RAIL	A01[#10(1)]
		77.27 ft.		

- A Full Description Of Each Part Is Listed Including The Room Number, Cabinet Number And Part Name
- Like Width Parts Are Listed From Longest To Shortest
- Like Size Parts Are Grouped Together
- The Total Lineal Footage Of Material At A Specific Width Is Listed

Figure 15-16 A computer-generated cutting list for face frames. (Courtesy of Cabinetware, Inc.)

DOOR CUTTING LIST

June 9, 1987   BINGHAM WOOD PRODUCTS   Page 4
                                      SMITH CUTTING LIST

FRAME AND PANEL DOORS

Finished Size (WxH)	Panel (WxH)	Top/Bottom Rails (WxL)	Stiles (WxL)	Room/Cabinet-Door
Panel Type:4/4 SOLID: OAK		Style:RAISED PANEL	Hinge:Left	
1) 23x37-1/2	1) 19-5/8x34-1/8	2) 2x19-7/8	2) 2x37-1/2	A01[#15-1]
1) 21-1/4x37-1/2	1) 17-7/8x34-1/8	2) 2x18-1/8	2)2x37-1/2	A01[#13-1]
1) 20-1/4x21-3/4	1) 16-7/8x18-3/8	2) 2x17-1/8	2) 2x21-3/4	A01[#3-1]
1) 18x61	1) 14-5/8x57-5/8	2) 2x14-7/8	2) 2x61	A01[#7-1]
1) 18x24-3/4	1) 14-5/8x21-3/8	2) 2x14-7/8	2) 2x24-3/4	A01[#7-2]
1) 18x21-3/4	1) 14-5/8x18-3/8	2) 2x14-7/8	2) 2x21-3/4	A01[#9-1]
		-- Hinge:Pair		
2) 18x21-1/2	2) 14-5/8x18-1/8	4) 2x14-7/8	4) 2x21-1/2	A01[#13-2]
2) 16-3/16x20-1/2	2) 12-13/16x17-1/8	4) 2x13-1/16	4) 2x20-1/2	A01[#2-1]
6) 15-15/16x42-7/8	6) 12-9/16x39-1/2	12) 2x12-13/16	12) 2x42-7/8	A01[#7-3/#8-1,2]
2) 15-7/16x21-3/4	2) 12-1/16x18-3/8	4) 2x12-5/16	4) 2x21-3/4	A01[#9-2]
2) 15x37-1/2	2) 11-5/8x34-1/8	4) 2x11-7/8	4) 2x37-1/2	A01[#10-1]
6) 14-15/16x37-1/2	6) 11-9/16x34-1/8	12) 2x11-13/16	12) 2x37-1/2	A01[#14-1,2,3]

- A Complete Cutlist Is Printed Out For Four Different Door Styles; Slab Doors With Or Without Edgebanding, Frame And Panel Doors, Buy Out Doors And Frame And Panel Doors With Matching Drawer Fronts
- The Overall Door Size For Each Door Is Listed
- The Hinging For Each Door Is Listed
- Each Door Is Identified By A Room Number, Cabinet Number And Door Number
- Like Width Parts Are Listed From Longest To Shortest
- Like Size Parts Are Grouped Together

Figure 15-17 A computer-generated cutting list for doors. (Courtesy of Cabinetware, Inc.)

DRAWER CUTTING LIST

| June 9, 1987 | | BINGHAM WOOD PRODUCTS
SMITH CUTTING LIST | | Page 5 |

DRAWERS

Fronts (HxW)	Sides (WxL)	Ends (WxL)	Bottoms (WxL)	Room/Cabinet-Drawer

Front Type:4/4 SOLID: OAK   Door Style:RAISED PANEL   Interior:5/8" MEL   Slide Type:GRANT 238 SLIDES

Fronts (HxW)	Sides (WxL)	Ends (WxL)	Bottoms (WxL)	Room/Cabinet-Drawer
4) 11-3/16x15-1/2	8) 9-11/16x22-3/8	4) 10-3/16x12-1/2	4) 12-15/16x21-11/16	A01[#7-D,E,F,G]
2) 10-3/8x23	4) 8-7/8x22-3/8	2) 9-3/8x20	2) 20-7/16x21-11/16	A01[#2-C,D]
2) 8-1/2x12	4) 7x22-3/8	2) 7-1/2x9	2) 9-7/16x21-11/16	A01[#6-A,B]
3) 5-1/2x32	6) 4x22-3/8	3) 4-1/2x29	3) 29-7/16x21-11/16	A01[#7-A,B,C]
3) 5-1/2x26	6) 4x22-3/8	3) 4-1/2x23	3) 23-7/16x21-11/16	A01[#4-A,B,C]
1) 5-1/2x23	2) 4x22-3/8	1) 4-1/2x20	1) 20-7/16x21-11/16	A01[#2-B]
1) 5-1/2x20-1/4	2) 4x22-3/8	1) 4-1/2x17-1/4	1) 17-11/16x21-11/16	A01[#3-A]
1) 5-1/2x11	2) 4x22-3/8	1) 4-1/2x8	1) 8-7/16x21-11/16	A01[#5-A]
4) 5-1/2x8-1/2	8) 4x22-3/8	4) 4-1/2x5-1/2	4) 5-15/16x21-11/16	A01[#9-A,B,D,E]

- Each Drawer Is Identified By A Room Number, Cabinet Number And Drawer Number
- Like Width Parts Are Listed From Longest To Shortest
- Like Size Parts Are Grouped Together

Figure 15-18 A computer-generated cutting list for drawers. (Courtesy of Cabinetware, Inc.)

panel saw. A program designed for a very large production shop would generate a program that gives a cutting layout based on cutting perhaps five sheets at a time on a horizontal panel saw. There may be overages on some part to allow getting the required parts while cutting five sheets at a time.

Some software companies' panel-cutting optimization programs can be loaded into the controllers for computer-controlled panel saws, eliminating the need for the operator to program the size, direction, and sequence of the cuts. All the operator has to do is start the saw to cut out the job.

It is easy to see why the payback time on computer investments is so short. The computer is a big aid in designing cabinets. It can then produce shop

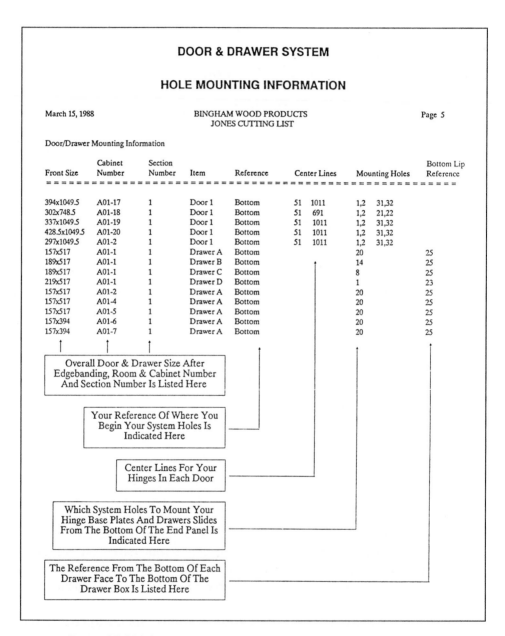

Figure 15-19 A computer-generated hole-mounting information sheet. (Courtesy of Cabinetware, Inc.)

MATERIAL COST LIST

March 15, 1988   BINGHAM WOOD PRODUCTS   Page 6
                                  JONES CUTTING LIST

MATERIALS COST LIST
DESCRIPTION   SQ. FEET   COST/FT.   COST
==

JOB TOTALS

Description	SQ. FEET	COST/FT.	COST
3/4" A2 OAK VENEER	26.64	$ 0.60	$ 15.98
3/4" A2 OAK VENEER	50.04	$ 0.65	$ 32.53
3/4" A2 VENEER: OAK	139.62	$ 0.69	$ 96.34
19 MM MELAMINE 1-S	346.94	$ 0.40	$ 138.77
6 MM MELAMINE 1-S	187.45	$ 0.25	$ 46.86
19 MM MELAMINE 2-S	88.82	$ 0.44	$ 39.08
13 MM MELAMINE 2-S	52.49	$ 0.37	$ 19.42
BLUM 110 (PR)	33	$ 1.97	$ 65.01
PULLS N.I.C.	48	$ 0.00	$ 0.00
BLUM 230E SLIDES (PR)	15	$ 3.12	$ 46.80
	========		==========
	892.01		$ 500.80

- Total Hardware Cost Including Drawer Slides, Hinges And Pulls
- Total Square Footage Of Each Material Type Including Waste
- Total Dollar Amount Of Each Material Type

Figure 15-20 A computer-generated material cost list. (Courtesy of Cabinetware, Inc.)

drawings, generate material-cutting lists, determine the best way to cut the material from sheets, and then instruct a computer-controlled saw to cut the part, all without any manual calculation! Computers also save much time and increase accuracy in estimating, and they can be a useful sales tool in showing prospective customers what their cabinets will look like.

Buying a computer system for the first time can be intimidating, but the standard computer advice—"Select the software that does what you want done and then buy a computer that will run that software"—applies to cabinetmaking as well.

There are several software companies that make excellent software packages designed just for cabinetmaking. They are usually represented at the larger woodworking shows and they advertise in the trade journals. Most cabinetmaking programs are designed for IBM or IBM-compatible computers. The exact hardware requirements vary with each software program because of individual complexities.

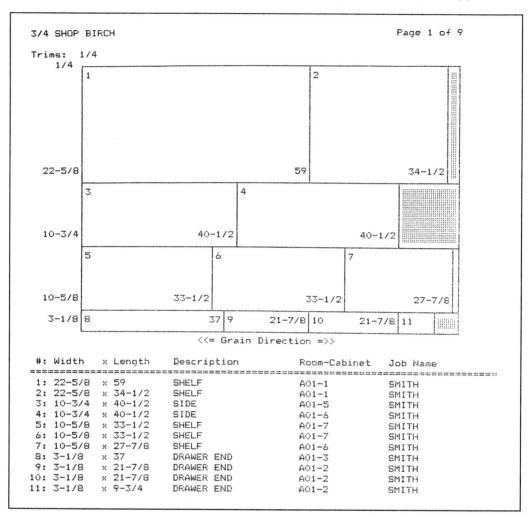

```
3/4 SHOP BIRCH                                                    Page 1 of 9

Trims:  1/4
      1/4
```

#:	Width	x Length	Description	Room-Cabinet	Job Name
1:	22-5/8	x 59	SHELF	A01-1	SMITH
2:	22-5/8	x 34-1/2	SHELF	A01-1	SMITH
3:	10-3/4	x 40-1/2	SIDE	A01-5	SMITH
4:	10-3/4	x 40-1/2	SIDE	A01-6	SMITH
5:	10-5/8	x 33-1/2	SHELF	A01-7	SMITH
6:	10-5/8	x 33-1/2	SHELF	A01-7	SMITH
7:	10-5/8	x 27-7/8	SHELF	A01-6	SMITH
8:	3-1/8	x 37	DRAWER END	A01-3	SMITH
9:	3-1/8	x 21-7/8	DRAWER END	A01-2	SMITH
10:	3-1/8	x 21-7/8	DRAWER END	A01-2	SMITH
11:	3-1/8	x 9-3/4	DRAWER END	A01-2	SMITH

Figure 15-21   A computer-generated panel-cutting plan. (Courtesy of Cabinetware, Inc.)

INDEX